CONTENTS

1989

SYMBOLS

RESERVATIONS ACCEPTED

FULL BAR

VALET PARKING

VIEW

ROMANTIC

LIVELY

DRESSY

LIVE ENTERTAINMENT

PRIVATE ROOM

OUTDOOR DINING

SPA CUISINE

NO SMOKING ANYWHERE

AVERAGE DINNER FOR TWO: Price quoted
does not include wine, tax and gratuity.

PRINTED IN KOREA

Own a bottle.

It's worth the price
to have at least one thing in your life
that's simply perfect.
Tanqueray. A singular experience.

EPICUREAN
Rendezvous

PUBLISHER
Richard Brault

CO-PUBLISHER
Cynthia Turnbull

EDITOR
Maia Madden

MANAGING EDITOR
Carla Detchon

CONTRIBUTING WRITERS
Mandy S. Page (San Francisco/Bay Area)
Patrick Franklin (Monterey/Carmel)
John Bonick (Wine Country)

ART DIRECTOR
Matthew Foster

ASSISTANT ART DIRECTOR
Bob Hoffman

ART ASSISTANTS
Kevin Brown   Patricia Fostar
Terry Oestreicher

PHOTOGRAPHER
Kingmond Young

PRODUCTION COORDINATOR
Kim D. Johnson

MARKETING DIRECTOR
Eleanor Phipps Price

MERCHANDISING DIRECTOR
Chris Fagg

ADVERTISING SALES MANAGER
Thierry Abel

PUBLIC RELATIONS
Karen Davis

CIRCULATION DIRECTOR
Richard Moxley

ACCOUNTING/BOOKKEEPING
Djaja Hardjadinata

DISTRIBUTION ASSISTANT
Dominic Mondi

TYPOGRAPHY
Zybert Graphics:
Jennifer Poole   Patrick Henderson
Gayle Zanca
CARTOGRAPHY
Eureka Cartography

AM/PM Publishing
2293 Filbert Street   San Francisco, CA 94123
TEL: 415.921.AMPM   FAX: 415.921.8050

E P I C U R E A N R E N D E Z V O U S

What It's All About

EPICUREAN RENDEZVOUS is an annual award program
and guide to the one hundred restaurants maintaining
the highest standards of cuisine and service in their
region. The Northern California guide is now in its third
edition, the Southern California in its first.

E very year, we evaluate hundreds of restaurants to determine which are the finest. We then present the winners with a framed award and include them in the guide free of charge. Restaurants do not pay for the write-up, the photography or the production of *Epicurean Rendezvous*. They are selected and judged strictly on merit.

An Advisory Board of twenty-five volunteer members, all food and wine experts, assists the staff of *Epicurean Rendezvous* in selecting award-winners. They propose and rate deserving new restaurants throughout the year and re-evaluate previous winners. Once a year, members of the Advisory Board meet to discuss their choices and cast a final vote on all restaurants under consideration.

RISING STARS

Certain criteria guide their decisions. "Rising Stars," those restaurants that have been in business less than three years, must meet the following conditions:

1. The restaurant must serve outstanding cuisine, striving for consistency.

2. The restaurant must show originality of concept and execution.

3. The decor must be clean, comfortable and attractive.

4. The staff must be courteous and must strive for consistently good service.

AWARD WINNERS

Established restaurants must meet at least five of these criteria:

1. The restaurant must serve consistently outstanding cuisine.

2. The chef must have at least five years of experience.

3. The staff must be knowledgeable and courteous and provide consistently excellent service.

4. The decor must be clean, comfortable and attractive.

5. The restaurant's wine list must have the depth,

Of all the gla

Gallé glass from the Perrier-Jouët Museum of the Belle Epoque, Epernay, France. To send a gift of Perrier-Jouët, call 1-800-238-4373.

breadth and balance to complement the cuisine.
6. The restaurant must have been in operation for at least three years under the same management.

Those award-winners who fail to maintain high standards or no longer meet the criteria are not presented with a new award or included in the next edition of *Epicurean Rendezvous*.

Those who wish to have their restaurants considered by *Epicurean Rendezvous* apply in writing or are suggested for review by the staff, the readers, the Advisory Board or the management of award-winning restaurants. Staff and Advisory Board members visit them incognito or are invited for an interview and/or inspection.

Once we have chosen our award-winners, we leave critique behind. Our goal is to promote and elevate those who work hard to maintain the standards of fine dining.

Think of our reviews as short guided tours of each restaurant. They put you inside the dining room and introduce you to the proprietor, manager or maitre d'. You meet the chef, learn a little about his or her cooking style, and look over a sample menu. By the time you sit down to enjoy a meal, the only surprises you'll encounter will be pleasant ones.

Epicurean Rendezvous is made possible by our many sponsors. They support our efforts to honor and promote the restaurant community. We thank them and those dedicated chefs and restaurant owners who have done so much to revolutionize America's cuisine.

We want *Epicurean Rendezvous* to be *your* favorite guide. Every year, we receive hundreds of letters from our readers telling us what they think about our book, our choice of award-winners or a particular restaurant. Your feedback is important. We urge you to write to us and to our member restaurants. And when you are making special plans, remember our free Rendezvous Reservations service.

Now that we have launched *Epicurean Rendezvous* in Southern California, the next stop is New York City. In the near future, *Epicurean Rendezvous* will cover every major metropolitan area in America.

■

lé created, only one has a work of art on the inside.

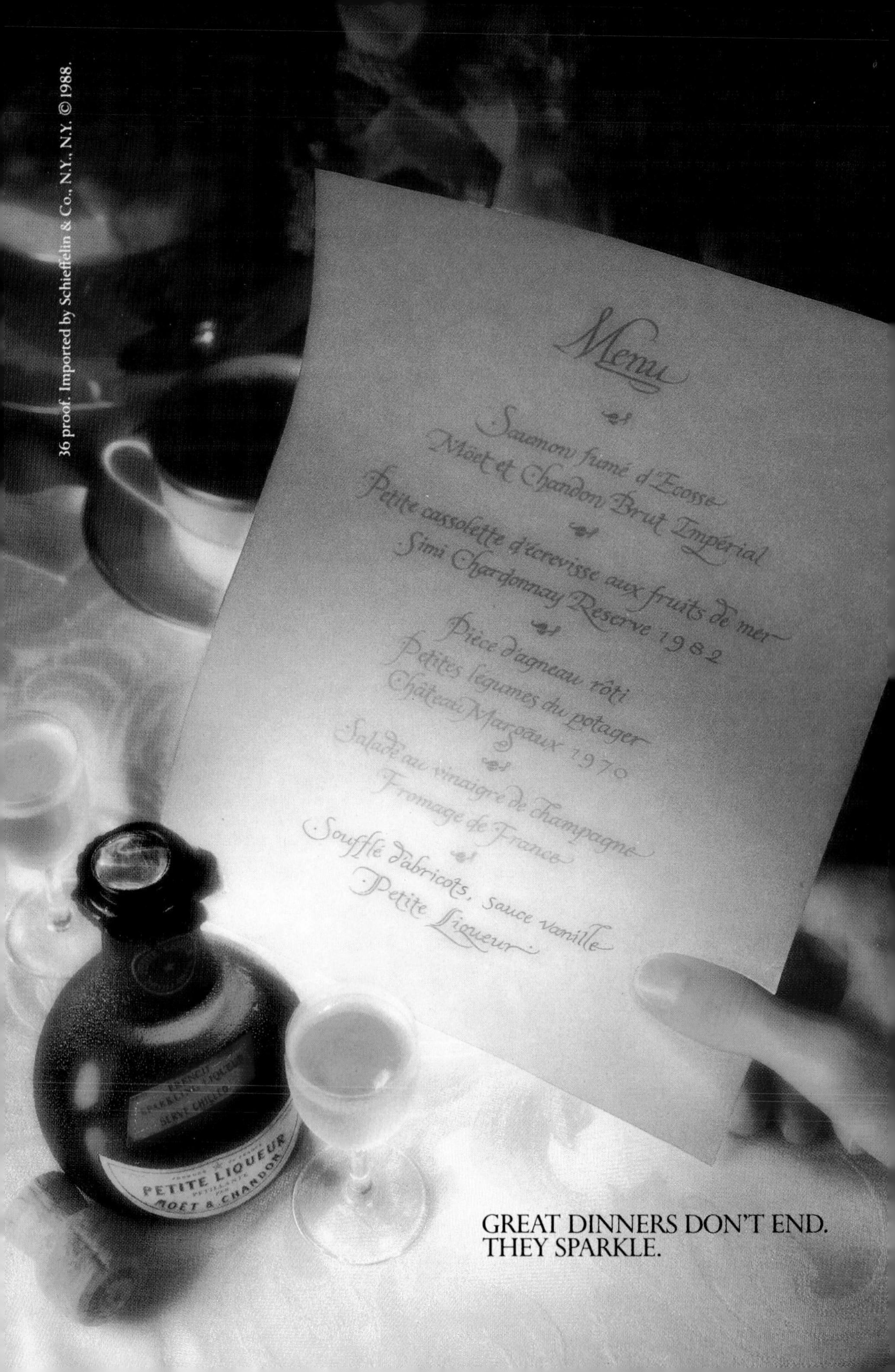

Menu

Saumon fumé d'Écosse
Möet et Chandon Brut Impérial

Petite cassolette d'écrevisse aux fruits de mer
Simi Chardonnay Reserve 1982

Pièce d'agneau rôti
Petites légumes du potager
Château Margaux 1970

Salade au vinaigre de Champagne
Fromage de France

Soufflé d'abricots, sauce vanille
Petite Liqueur

PETITE LIQUEUR
MOËT & CHANDON

**GREAT DINNERS DON'T END.
THEY SPARKLE.**

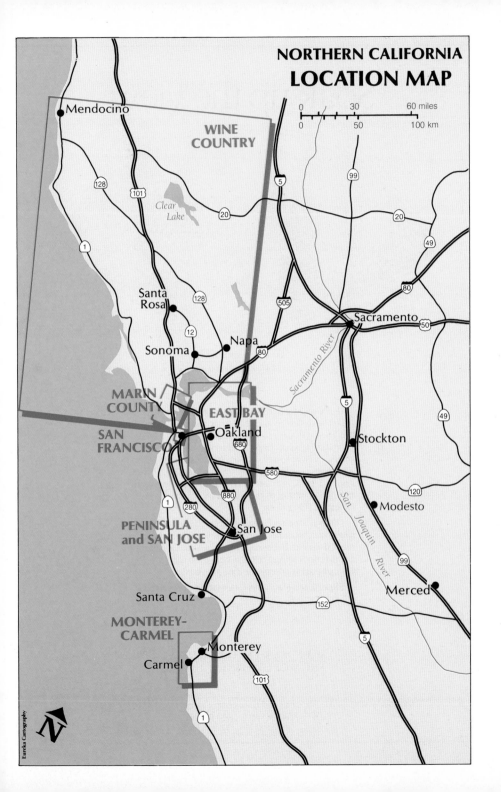

NORTHERN CALIFORNIA
LOCATION MAP

WINE COUNTRY

MARIN COUNTY

EAST BAY

SAN FRANCISCO

PENINSULA and SAN JOSE

MONTEREY-CARMEL

Mendocino

Clear Lake

Santa Rosa

Sonoma

Napa

Sacramento

Sacramento River

Oakland

Stockton

Modesto

San Joaquin River

San Jose

Santa Cruz

Merced

Monterey

Carmel

Eureka Cartography

0   30   60 miles
0   50   100 km

Soak up the view.

MANDARIN ORIENTAL
SAN FRANCISCO

Discover Mandarin Oriental, a private world rising high above the Financial District and occupying the top eleven floors of the prestigious 48-story First Interstate Center. Just 160 select guestrooms and suites, in twin towers, linked by spectacular glass skybridges — offering only seven rooms per tower floor. Elegant, intimate, charming. All presented in the rich tradition of the legendary Mandarin Oriental, Hong Kong.

Smooth Mediterranean marble. Elegant English toiletries. And a breathtaking view of one of the most dramatic backdrops in the world. Our guests are discriminating travelers who look for exceptional accommodations and service.

Experience Mandarin Oriental, San Francisco.

MANDARIN ORIENTAL
THE WORLD'S FINEST HOTELS

Mandarin Oriental, San Francisco   222 Sansome Street   San Francisco CA 94104
(415) 885-0999   (800) 622-0404
A member of *The Leading Hotels of the World*®

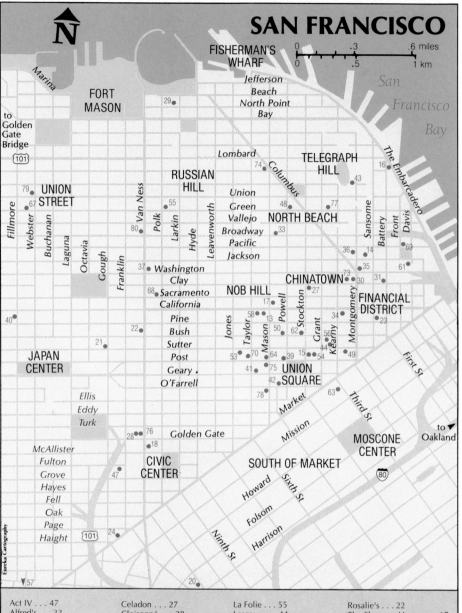

SAN FRANCISCO

FISHERMAN'S WHARF

0 .3 .6 miles
0 .5 1 km

San Francisco Bay

FORT MASON

Marina

to Golden Gate Bridge
[101]

29

Jefferson
Beach
North Point
Bay

Lombard
74 Columbus

TELEGRAPH HILL

16

43

RUSSIAN HILL

Union
Green
Vallejo
Broadway
Pacific
Jackson

79 **UNION STREET**
67

Fillmore
Webster
Buchanan
Laguna
Octavia
Gough
Franklin
Van Ness
Polk
Larkin
Hyde
Leavenworth

55
80

48 77
NORTH BEACH
33

The Embarcadero
Sansome
Battery
Front
Davis

36   14
73   35
30   31
69
61

CHINATOWN

37 Washington
Clay
68 Sacramento
California
Pine
Bush
Sutter
Post
Geary
O'Farrell

NOB HILL

27

17
58 13
50
62
34
FINANCIAL DISTRICT
23

40

22
21

Jones
Taylor
Mason
Powell
Stockton
Grant
Kearny
Montgomery

JAPAN CENTER

53 70 64 39 15 54 49
41 75 **UNION SQUARE**
42
78
63

First St
Third St

Ellis
Eddy
Turk

Market
Mission

28 76 Golden Gate
18

MOSCONE CENTER
[80]

to Oakland

McAllister
Fulton
Grove
Hayes
Fell
Oak
Page
Haight

47

CIVIC CENTER

SOUTH OF MARKET

Howard
Sixth St
Folsom
Ninth St
Harrison

[101]
24

Eureka Cartography

57

20

Numbers correspond to location on map above and page numbers in guide

INDULGENT. THE SENSE OF REMY.

REMY MARTIN

CUVÉE DE FRANCE   DEPUIS 1724   80 PROOF
                                        750 ml

Rémy Martin

COGNAC

FRANCE

E REMY MARTIN & Co COGNAC FRANCE

FINE CHAMPAGNE COGNAC

Exclusively Fine Champagne Cognac

THE BIG FOUR

HUNTINGTON HOTEL
1075 CALIFORNIA STREET
SAN FRANCISCO, CA 94108
(415) 771-1140

Major Credit Cards
Open Daily · Breakfast, Lunch & Dinner

Manager
Newton A. Cope, Jr.

Chef
Gloria Ciccarone

All of his life, Newton A. Cope, Sr., was captivated by the colorful history of the "Big Four": C.P. Huntington, Charles Crocker, Mark Hopkins and Leland Stanford, railroad men who built their empires after 1869 and became San Francisco's wealthiest, most influential citizens. Eleven years ago, he opened The Big Four in the Huntington Hotel and filled the restaurant with his extensive collection of California art, Big Four political cartoons, railroad prints and other historical memorabilia.

Restaurant Manager Newton A. Cope, Jr., has strived to establish a culinary reputation for The Big Four equal to the old-world traditions championed by his father.

With the help of Chef Gloria Ciccarone, that reputation is assured. "We are recep-tive to innovation here, especially with our daily specials," she says, "but we pride ourselves on serving a traditional American menu that changes with the seasons." AVERAGE DINNER FOR TWO: $70

Menu Highlights

SEASONAL MENU

Appetizers

Smoked pheasant & mango salad *
Gravlax with mustard, lemon & fennel
sauce * Fresh bufala mozzarella with
basil & virgin olive oil

Entrées

Roast Barbarie duck breast with
kumquat, honey & peppercorn glaze *
Roast prime rib of angus beef * Saddle
of antelope with fresh huckleberries

BIX

56 GOLD STREET
AT MONTGOMERY
SAN FRANCISCO, CA 94133
(415) 433-6300

MasterCard & Visa Only
Open Daily for Dinner · Lunch Mon-Fri

Proprietor
Doug Biederbeck

Chef
Gordon Drysdale

To reach the newest hot spot in San Francisco, go down a quiet alley off Montgomery Street near Jackson Square to a plain brick building flanked by antique galleries. Inside is Bix, a tribute to the Jazz Age and Art Moderne that Doug ("Bix") Biederbeck calls "an updated supper club," complete with torch singer, saxophone player and jazz pianist.

A huge, deep-hued mural of a jazz club scene is the focal point of the restaurant. Underneath, behind the always-jammed bar, white-jacketed bartenders ring in the renaissance of the cocktail with deftly prepared Manhattans, Sidecars and Martinis.

Bix recalls the era of the majestic ocean liner, with curving Honduras mahogany, silver columns and reproductions of late 1920s ceiling lamps.

The menu is filled with offerings that sound simple and straightforward. Modern culinary flourishes jazz up each one, to surprise and delight the palate. AVERAGE DINNER FOR TWO: $50

Menu Highlights

Appetizers

Sweet corn custard ∗ Sonoma foie gras with artichoke heart ∗ Waldorf salad with blue cheese ∗ Steak tartare ∗ American sturgeon caviar with blini

Entrées

Salmon with mushrooms in truffle oil ∗ Pork chop with mashed potatoes & garden peas ∗ Lamb chops with mint & onions ∗ Grilled Maine lobster ∗ Pan-fried chicken cutlet with capers ∗ Chicken hash

AMERICAN

CAMPTON PLACE

340 STOCKTON STREET
NEAR SUTTER
SAN FRANCISCO, CA 94108
(415) 781-5155

Major Credit Cards
Open Daily • Breakfast, Lunch & Dinner

Maitre d'
Chloe Warren

Chef
Bradley M. Ogden

In recent years, the best hotels have made major efforts to develop fine restaurants that attract local patrons as well as guests. A brilliant success in this vein is Union Square's Campton Place Hotel and Restaurant. The dining room is a comfortable design of banquettes and walls upholstered in peach, gray and ivory tones with a splash of chocolate brown. Mirrors, plush carpeting, sprays of flowers and tall windows add a light and airy elegance.

Bradley M. Ogden, exemplifying the new born-in-America chef, is a graduate of the Culinary Institute of America. Presenting a mixture of homespun and classic American cuisine, he says, "I've taken some traditional recipes and added creative ideas of my own to make them different. We then incorporate the best seasonal ingredients in a regularly changing menu." Rediscover the joy of a morning meal with one of Chef Ogden's hearty Midwestern breakfasts. AVERAGE DINNER FOR TWO: $80

Menu Highlights

MONTHLY MENU

Appetizers

Lobster strudel with chive butter ∗ Thai quail salad with Chinese egg noodles ∗ Fried soft shell crab with black bean salsa

Entrées

Grilled salmon with shrimp corn fritters ∗ Roast lamb loin with fennel ratatouille & wild onion cakes ∗ Grilled veal chop with pepper linguine

FOG CITY DINER

1300 BATTERY STREET
AT EMBARCADERO
SAN FRANCISCO, CA 94133
(415) 982-2000

Master Card & Visa Only
Open Daily · Lunch & Dinner

Proprietor
Bill Higgins

Chef/Proprietor
Cindy Pawlcyn

As a child in Chicago, says Bill Higgins, "the diner was the first restaurant I understood. The food was accessible, and I liked being able to watch the cooks." When Higgins grew up, he opened his very own diner, with updated diner food and such adult touches as a full bar and a sexy, streamlined interior.

With its chrome and neon facade, Fog City Diner is a trendsetter, one of the first restaurants to encourage patrons to sample its specialties by sharing a variety of appetizers. Cindy Pawlcyn's menu centers around "small plates" made for "grazing," a practice now popular in restaurants around the country.

If you prefer traditional diner fare, you won't be disappointed. The menu is full of middle-American favorites like milk-shakes and chili dogs, made modern but not *nouvelle*. Fog City's success has spawned lots of neo-diners imitating its inspired menu and sleek decor. But don't be fooled — there's no topping the original. AVERAGE DINNER FOR TWO: $65

Menu Highlights

Appetizers

Crabcakes with sherry-cayenne mayonnaise * Garlic custard with mushrooms, chives & chopped seasoned walnuts * Grilled stuffed Pasilla pepper with avocado salsa

Entrées

Several salads on a plate * Grilled skirt steak with tomato aioli * Diner chili dog * Grilled sesame chicken with shiitake mushrooms, carrots & Chinese mustard

AMERICAN

MASONS

FAIRMONT HOTEL
950 MASON STREET
SAN FRANCISCO, CA 94108
(415) 392-0113

Major Credit Cards
Open Daily · Dinner Only

☎ 🍸 🚗 📷 🍴 📹 🎵 🅿️

General Manager
Peter Seely

Chef
Paul Wiggins

Masons Restaurant has changed from what used to be an American broiler with a Japanese/Polynesian theme to a glamorous, inviting restaurant serving regional American cuisine. "This is what I've been working toward all along," says Peter Seely.

Completely renovated in 1987 by internationally known designer Louis Cataffo, Masons now has the look of a residential dining room, with comfortable banquettes, lovely window tables, gleaming brass fixtures and an expanse of blond Japanese butterfly oak. Framed prints of monkeys and large handpainted murals add a lighthearted note. The ambiance is just the way Seely likes it: casual, friendly and decidedly unstuffy.

Chef Paul Wiggins, most recently of St. George Restaurant in St. Helena, has designed a menu that is equally accommodating. Diners can choose from health-conscious, simply broiled entrees or seasonal chef's specialties, or create an entire meal from an array of inspired appetizers. AVERAGE DINNER FOR TWO: $65

Menu Highlights

SEASONAL MENU

Appetizers
Southern corn & lobster fritter ∗ Duck-filled tamales ∗ Sashimi ∗ Fried noodles, papaya & Bay shrimp on baby greens with ginger-chive dressing

Entrées
Fresh rabbit braised in Zinfandel with three chiles & coriander ∗ Sautéed duck breast with candied lemon rind & honey ginger glaze ∗ Broiled fresh Pacific fish

STARS

150 REDWOOD ALLEY
NEAR VAN NESS
SAN FRANCISCO, CA 94102
(415) 861-7827

Major Credit Cards
Open Daily • Lunch & Dinner

Dining Rm. Manager
Tony Angotti
Business Manager
Steve Vranian

Chef
Bradford Barker
Executive Chef
Mark Franz

Here, within a spacious room housing an open kitchen, two elevated dining areas, a grand piano and an always packed cocktail area, you will discover Stars—at the counter, at the tables, on the wine list and, most importantly, in the kitchen.

Chef Jeremiah Tower fell in love with culinary art at a very early age and later decided food, wine and meeting people were the aspects of life he most enjoyed. In 1972, he became chef at Chez Panisse and later co-owner.

In 1984, he created Stars, near San Francisco's civic and cultural center, to provide performers with a haven of exciting food, wine and ambiance. Says Tower, "San Franciscans like to go to the same place frequently, but they also need the new and exciting."

Stars is the kind of place where people are equally at home in jeans or a tuxedo. If you're in a hurry, try Starfish, which features Australian-style fish and chips to go. AVERAGE DINNER FOR TWO: $70

Menu Highlights

DAILY MENU

Appetizers

Giant shiitake mushroom cap with buttered lobster, celery root & chile sauce ∗ Crab cakes with grilled tomato sauce, papaya relish & chipolte cream

Entrées

Sautéed spicy Louisiana prawns with coconut-chile rice, black bean sauce & mango salsa ∗ Grilled lamb chops with minted couscous, garlic cream & fig relish

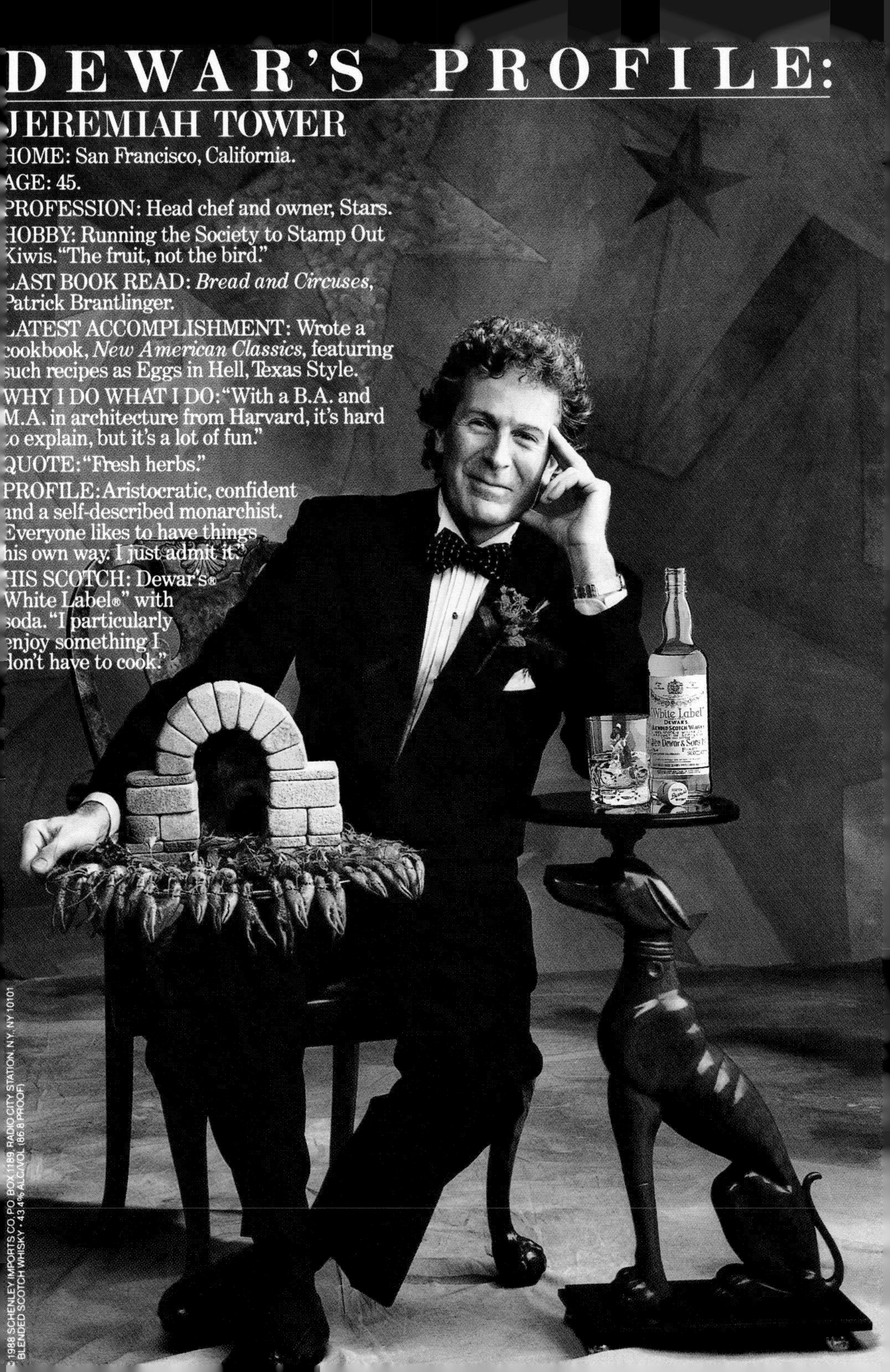

DEWAR'S PROFILE:

JEREMIAH TOWER

HOME: San Francisco, California.

AGE: 45.

PROFESSION: Head chef and owner, Stars.

HOBBY: Running the Society to Stamp Out Kiwis. "The fruit, not the bird."

LAST BOOK READ: *Bread and Circuses,* Patrick Brantlinger.

LATEST ACCOMPLISHMENT: Wrote a cookbook, *New American Classics,* featuring such recipes as Eggs in Hell, Texas Style.

WHY I DO WHAT I DO: "With a B.A. and M.A. in architecture from Harvard, it's hard to explain, but it's a lot of fun."

QUOTE: "Fresh herbs."

PROFILE: Aristocratic, confident and a self-described monarchist. "Everyone likes to have things his own way. I just admit it."

HIS SCOTCH: Dewar's® White Label® with soda. "I particularly enjoy something I don't have to cook."

TAXI

374 11TH STREET
AT HARRISON
SAN FRANCISCO, CA 94103
(415) 558-TAXI

Major Credit Cards
Open Daily for Dinner • Lunch Mon-Fri

Proprietors
John Crucianelli &
William Whitmore

Chef
Timothy Ottaviani

It took Will Whitmore and partner John Crucianelli four months to clean, paint, install a kitchen and salvage the original fir floor of their South of Market warehouse. One night while working late, Whitmore looked across the street at the line of cabs in front of the DNA Lounge and knew what he was going to name his restaurant.

Today, Taxi is a bright beacon that draws a diverse crowd from all over The City. Its white, purposefully unadorned walls offer no distractions from the stylish food. As Whitmore says, "There's no need to complicate things—it's always best to leave them simple."

Taxi's menu is the only adornment the restaurant needs. A blend of California and American cuisines, meals are uncontrived with an emphasis on generous por-

tions. For a more intimate experience, be sure to try the wine bar in the back.
AVERAGE DINNER FOR TWO: $55

Menu Highlights

DAILY MENU
Appetizers

Market greens salad with fresh herbs, sweet tomatoes, nasturtiums & smoked trout butter toasts * Marinated watermelon & red onion salad with raspberry vinaigrette

Entrées

Sweetbread coulibiac with basmati rice, peppers, baby vegetables & sundried tomato béarnaise * Fresh prawn & sea scallop ragout with black pepper fetuccine

CAFÉ MAJESTIC

THE MAJESTIC HOTEL
1500 SUTTER STREET
SAN FRANCISCO, CA 94109
(415) 776-6400

Major Credit Cards
Closed Monday • Breakfast, Lunch & Dinner

CALIFORNIA

Proprietors
Tom Marshall & Rolf Lewis

Chef
Peter DeMarais
Chef/Proprietor
Stanley Eichelbaum

For many years, Stanley Eichelbaum, the *Examiner* theatre critic who gave up his career to attend the California Culinary Academy, collected rare old San Francisco cookbooks, including Victor Hirtzler's 1910 *St. Francis Hotel Cookbook,* which he recently had a hand in reissuing. He took such pleasure in experimenting with vintage recipes that he made this his specialty.

When he and Tom Marshall opened Café Majestic three years ago, they dedicated the menu to the old California cuisine Eichelbaum had discovered. With the help of Chef Peter DeMarais, Eichelbaum took his favorite recipes and fine-tuned them to today's palate. They sprinkled the menu with such new California creations as gourmet pizza, and offered outstanding desserts.

The Majestic Hotel's stately yet graceful dining room suits this cuisine perfectly. Restored to its 1902 splendor by local artisans, the Café Majestic has a beautiful bar that dates back 125 years and was imported from Paris. AVERAGE DINNER FOR TWO: $65

Menu Highlights

SEASONAL MENU

Appetizers

Warm quail salad Yerba Buena on limestone lettuce with ruby grapefruit & mint-sherry vinaigrette ∗ Lobster & scallop ravioli, sauce Américaine

Entrées

Grilled chicken Nellie Melba with lychee nuts & wild mushrooms ∗ Grilled veal chop with fresh sage & melted Bleu d'Auvergne

ROSALIE'S

1415 VAN NESS AVENUE
AT BUSH
SAN FRANCISCO, CA 94109
(415) 928-7188

Major Credit Cards
Open Daily • Dinner Only

Manager
Brett Kladney

Executive Chef
Rick O'Connell

Brett Kladney was coming out of a movie theatre when he happened to run into Rosalie's. "It was unlike any restaurant I'd ever seen before," he says, "dramatic and striking." Soon Kladney was going to the restaurant every night. When owner William Miller offered him a job, he readily accepted.

Rosalie's has that effect on a lot of people. The decor, designed by Amy McGill, must be seen to be believed. Concrete "drapes" line the outside of the building, while inside, galvanized steel palm trees and tables, beige leather banquettes and stuffed dummies create a wacky yet appealing Southern California ambiance that quickly turns occasional patrons into regulars.

The enticing regional cuisine of Chef Rick O'Connell can certainly hold its own in this environment. O'Connell draws on the traditions of Southwestern, New England, Southern, Cajun/Creole and Midwestern cooking, adding contemporary techniques to create a fresh, new American cuisine. AVERAGE DINNER FOR TWO: $65

Menu Highlights

SEASONAL MENU

Appetizers

Grilled quail on spicy corncakes with passionfruit sauce * Rosalie's coleslaw taco with peanuts, blueberries & ancho chile mayonnaise

Entrées

Steamed salmon with raspberry butter sauce & smoked salmon rice croquette * Grilled loin of lamb with barbecued lamb ribs

SILKS

MANDARIN ORIENTAL HOTEL
222 SANSOME STREET
SAN FRANCISCO, CA 94104
(415) 986-2020

Major Credit Cards
Open Daily · Breakfast, Lunch & Dinner

General Manager
Wolfgang K. Hültner

Executive Chef
Howard Bulka

Visitors cross an opulent green and white marble lobby and ascend an elegant staircase to reach Silks. The centerpiece of the dining room is an octagonal copper and brass table loaded with fruits, vegetables, breads, wines and liqueurs. Waiters in brocade vests pass silently by luxe tables in secluded niches.

In this grand Oriental setting, the cuisine comes as a refreshing surprise. The powers that be at the Mandarin Oriental wanted a restaurant that served California cuisine of a caliber that would attract the hard-to-please local clientele. In Silks, they have succeeded.

"I like to introduce a bit of wit and whimsy into the menu," says Bulka, formerly of L.A.'s celebrated La Toque restaurant. Strongly rooted in French tech-niques, having studied with Master Chefs Paul Bocuse and Alain Chapel in France, Bulka describes his cuisine as "fresh, light, fun, colorful and full of strong flavors." AVERAGE DINNER FOR TWO: $60

Menu Highlights

BI-WEEKLY MENU

Appetizers
Hash brown potatoes with crème fraiche
& gold caviar ∗ Shrimp & corn chowder

Entrées
Roast rack of lamb with ratatouille &
risotto custard ∗ Grilled sea scallops
with oven-roasted tomatoes & zucchini-
mushroom pancakes ∗ Monkfish pan-
roasted with pearl onions, bacon &
French apple cider

ZUNI CAFE

1658 MARKET STREET
AT FRANKLIN
SAN FRANCISCO, CA 94102
(415) 552-2522

Major Credit Cards
Closed Monday · Breakfast, Lunch & Dinner

☎ 🍸 🎶 🎵 ⚓

Proprietors
William West & Vince Calcagno

Chef
Judy Rodgers

The Zuni Café is twice as big and beautiful as when it opened ten years ago, yet it retains its unpretentious style and eclectic clientele. New hours, from early morning until midnight, and a California/Mediterranean lunch and dinner menu that changes daily attract a nonstop parade of diners. On sunny days or warm evenings, the café's Paris-style sidewalk tables, all too rare in San Francisco, are ideal for people-watching.

The kitchen is in the capable hands of Judy Rodgers. Rodgers got hooked on cooking during a high school exchange to Roanne, France, where she stayed with the owners of Les Frères Troisgros. "I spent every minute I could in the restaurant kitchen!" She earned a degree from Stanford, but it wasn't long before Alice Waters asked her to work at Chez Panisse. After three years, Rodgers returned to apprentice in southwestern France, and has been cooking ever since. AVERAGE DINNER FOR TWO: $55

Menu Highlights

DAILY MENU

Appetizers

House-cured anchovies with parmesan & celery * Spicy squid stew with red wine & basil

Entrées

Fusili with charred tomatoes, hot pepper, pancetta & bread crumbs * Chicken roasted in the brick oven with bread salad * Risotto with lobster, fresh shell beans & sage

JOY
de
BAIN

JEAN PATOU
PARIS

JOY

NORDSTROM

I'll be crushed if I don't get picked by Laurent-Perrier.

You'll be crushed if you do.

Grand Siècle Champagne

From Laurent-Perrier

CHINESE

CELADON

881 CLAY STREET
AT STOCKTON
SAN FRANCISCO, CA 94108
(415) 982-1168

Major Credit Cards
Open Daily • Lunch & Dinner

Proprietor
James Ho

Manager
Nick Wong

Celadon, porcelain created by legendary artists of the T'ang Dynasty, circa 618-906 AD, is a fitting name for this renowned Chinese restaurant. Celadon porcelain dinnerware, pale lime linens and intricately detailed flatware adorn each table, while hand-carved wooden chairs inset with mother-of-pearl designs provide an Imperial touch. A large mural depicting the story of the Seven Ladies of China dominates the multileveled dining and lounge areas.

Cantonese cuisine, the primary cooking style here, repeats this harmony with its balance of color, aroma and flavor. Chef Lom Kan, trained in the Master Chef/Four Kings tradition, creates a dining experience reminiscent of ancient China.

The Celadon is a dining favorite at Chinese New Year and other special occasions; you will vie for a table there with the likes of Miss Chinatown and business and social leaders in the Chinese community. AVERAGE DINNER FOR TWO: $50

Menu Highlights

Appetizers

Tender marinated quail flamed with brandy at your table ＊ Soft-shell crab ＊ Escargots with Szechuan sauce ＊ Seafood bisque steamed in coconut shell

Entrées

Peking duck, carved at your table ＊ Steamed lobster, Celadon style ＊ Shrimp & pinenuts in a lettuce leaf ＊ Lichee chicken, deep-fried in a light water chestnut batter, served with lichees & sweet & sour sauce

CHINESE

CLOISONNE

601 VAN NESS AVENUE
AT OPERA PLAZA
SAN FRANCISCO, CA 94102
(415) 441-2232

Major Credit Cards
Open Daily • Lunch & Dinner

Proprietors
Doug Wong & James Ho
General Manager
Vonica Yee

Chefs
Johnson Young & Long Wong

With the opening of Cloisonné, the Civic Center area has at last acquired a first-class Cantonese restaurant. Just minutes from the opera, symphony and ballet, it is an opulent yet comfortable destination for lunch, dinner, a late-night snack or a relaxing drink at the bar.

"The art of cloisonné reflects my concept of East meets West," says James Ho, owner of the prestigious Celadon restaurant and Deputy Mayor of San Francisco. "Different little pieces fitting together to create something beautiful."

He and partner Doug Wong have created an airy blend of Chinese art and appointments and sophisticated marble and glass. A handpainted ceiling depicts a colorful dragon, and jade plate-stands and cloisonné chopsticks adorn the rosewood tables. Two private dining rooms make luxurious settings for a real Chinese feast.

The only restaurant in San Francisco where you can have dim sum for dinner, Cloisonné is open until midnight. AVERAGE DINNER FOR TWO: $45

Menu Highlights

Appetizers

Cloisonné chicken salad * Szechuan escargots * Minced oysters in green purse * Peppered calamari * Shark's fin soup

Entrées

Chicken steamed in lotus * Peking duck * Barbecued young quail * Kwang-hsi stir-fried squab * Clay pot spareribs * Honeyed walnuts & scallops * Clams in black bean sauce * Fresh steamed lobster with ginger & scallions

THE MANDARIN

900 NORTH POINT
GHIRARDELLI SQUARE
SAN FRANCISCO, CA 94109
(415) 673-8812

Major Credit Cards
Open Daily • Lunch & Dinner

Proprietor
Cecilia Chiang

Chef
Teh Jong Ko

Ghirardelli Square, the former chocolate factory and warehouse near Fisherman's Wharf, is also home to The Mandarin, the first restaurant in the United States to serve Szechuan and Northern Chinese cuisine. Huge pillars, imposing stone fountains, quarried floor tiles, luxurious Oriental carpets, petit point tapestries and stone and wood-hewn statues recall the grandeur of pre-revolutionary China.

It is an apt setting for Chiang's world-famous cuisine. Raised in Peking, Madame Chiang learned the fine art of preparing the duck specialty of that region, and went on to develop her own incomparable version by smoking it in special ovens over burning tea leaves. In addition, the menu offers nearly 250 authentic Szechuan, Hunan and Mandarin selections,

each superbly prepared by Chef Teh Jong Ko. After twenty-two years of consistently fine cuisine and service, Cecilia Chiang and The Mandarin are still the toast of San Francisco. AVERAGE DINNER FOR TWO: $50

Menu Highlights

Appetizers
Minced squab ∗ Mandarin spareribs ∗
Crab claws ∗ Spring rolls

Entrées
Peking duck served with Chinese paoping,
scallions & plum sauce (24 hrs. notice) ∗
Beggar's chicken: a fowl finely flavored,
encased in clay & baked (24 hrs. notice) ∗
Pork à la Szechuan ∗ Seafood basket:
scallops, prawns & abalone sautéed with
vegetables in a rice wine sauce

C
H
I
N
E
S
E

TOMMY TOY'S

655 MONTGOMERY STREET
AT WASHINGTON
SAN FRANCISCO, CA 94108
(415) 397-4888

Major Credit Cards
Dinner Mon-Sat · Lunch Mon-Fri

Proprietor
Tommy Toy

Chef
Ken Wu

Fifteen years after he opened the highly successful Imperial Palace, Tommy Toy has done it again with his very own Tommy Toy's. This time, he has created a sumptuous restaurant off the beaten track, "for discriminating people who want an elegant French touch to their Chinese cuisine."

You won't find chopsticks here, only silverware, porcelain, authentic Chinese bridal lamps, and an incomparable display of Chinese pottery and art from the private collection of Toy's partner, Joe Yuey. Toy, trained as an interior decorator, has recreated the opulence of the nineteenth-century Empress Dowager's reading room, with ancient "Powder Paintings" framed in sandalwood and antique wooden hand-carved archways from mainland China.

The food here is no less opulent, Cantonese and Szechuan dishes refined by Toy's own palate. Ask him to design your dinner menu himself, and you will enjoy a most memorable meal. AVERAGE DINNER FOR TWO: $50

Menu Highlights

SEASONAL MENU

Appetizers

Rice-paper-wrapped shrimp with foie gras ∗ Chinese crêpes rolled with shredded roasted duck & spicy vegetables ∗ Escargots Chinoise

Entrees

Diced chicken with pinenuts in a light pepper sauce ∗ Peking duck with Chinese crêpes ∗ Tenderloin of veal sautéed with roasted pecans ∗ Deep-fried fresh pears with garlic, scallops & fresh mushrooms

YANK SING

427 BATTERY STREET
AT WASHINGTON
SAN FRANCISCO, CA 94111
(415) 362-1640

Major Credit Cards
Open Daily ＊ Lunch Only

Proprietor
Henry Chan

Chefs
K.M. Tse, Helen Chan &
Wayne Tang

By now, most aficionados of Chinese cuisine are familiar with dim sum, those exquisite Cantonese delicacies that have captured the imagination of Western gourmets. Dim sum are the thousand-year-old legacy of an enterprising chef of the Sung Dynasty whose emperor asked to sample all the cuisines of China in one meal. He invented miniature versions of regional favorites that would tempt the eye as well as the palate, hence the name dim sum, or "heart's delight."

The evolution of dim sum continues at Yank Sing, where owners Henry and Judy Chan have created a serene, refined atmosphere in which to sample these delicacies. "Dim sum is a cuisine of constant experimentation, with hundreds of variations," says Henry Chan.

Every morning he consults with his chefs on what to change, add or improvise from their eighty-item repertoire, for a menu that changes as frequently as the carts of dim sum roll out of the kitchen.

AVERAGE LUNCH FOR TWO: $25

Menu Highlights

Dim Sum

＊ Stuffed crab claw
＊ Yank Sing won ton
＊ Spring roll
＊ Shrimp roll
＊ Potstickers
＊ Seafood with cream cheese
＊ Silver-wrapped chicken
＊ Shrimp dumpling
＊ Mandarin dumpling with chives
＊ Four color siu mye

GET THE VIP TREATMENT
YOU DESERVE

CALL

RENDEZVOUS

RESERVATIONS

Restaurant Information and Reservation Service.
Person-to-person details on
Northern California's outstanding restaurants.
Type of cuisine . . . Ambiance . . . Location . . . Special Occasions

ALL IN ONE CALL AND ABSOLUTELY FREE!
9:00am-6:00pm Monday through Friday
(415) 921-AMPM

ALFRED'S

886 BROADWAY
AT WESTBOUND BROADWAY TUNNEL
SAN FRANCISCO, CA 94133
(415) 781-7058

Major Credit Cards
Open Daily for Dinner · Lunch Thursday Only

Proprietor
Art Petri

Proprietor
Al Petri

Since 1928, Alfred's has served only the finest prime cuts of juicy corn-fed, skillfully aged steaks broiled over imported Mexican mesquite charcoal, producing tender, distinctively flavorful meat. Owner Al Petri recommends a tangy Caesar salad and an order of tortellini in a creamy pesto sauce as a start to dinner.

At Alfred's, customers deliberate whether to order beef, veal, chicken or seafood and whether to have it mesquite-grilled or prepared in traditional Italian style (the cannelloni and fetuccine here are evidence of the North Beach-Italian tradition maintained at Alfred's).

A thoroughly professional staff provides personal, attentive service in a rich club-like atmosphere that exudes Victorian luxury. Upstairs, banquet rooms can handle private parties of fifteen to fifty. Alfred's, meat-and-potatoes Americana with an Italian touch, is an enduring San Francisco institution. AVERAGE DINNER FOR TWO: $55

Menu Highlights

Appetizers

Escargots Bourguignonne ∗ Italian fried calamari ∗ Fresh oysters, half shell ∗ Caesar salad ∗ Fresh artichoke

Entrées

Alfred's bone-in New York steak ∗ Châteaubriand of beef tenderloin, sauce béarnaise, carved at the table ∗ Porterhouse steak ∗ Filet mignon of beef tenderloin ∗ Chicago rib eye steak ∗ Fresh salmon, mesquite-broiled

CARNELIAN ROOM

BANK OF AMERICA BUILDING
555 CALIFORNIA STREET
SAN FRANCISCO CA 94104
(415) 433-7500

Major Credit Cards
Open Daily for Dinner · Sunday Brunch

🕿 🍸 🖃 📷 🍴 🅥 🅿🆁

Manager
Marvin Israel

Chef
Gabriel Elicethe

Soaring fifty-two stories above San Francisco's financial district, The Carnelian Room offers a panoramic view of the Bay Area. The Bank of America's polished granite building is a fitting home for this elegant dining establishment.

General Manager Marvin Israel has guided the restaurant on its elevated course of excellence since it opened seventeen years ago. Chef Gabriel Elicethe, trained in France's Basque Country, changes his menu twice yearly and his specials every day to fully utilize California's rich variety of vegetables, fruit, seafood, fowl, beef and game.

By day, the Carnelian Room is the exclusive Banker's Club, accessible only to members or by invitation. The restaurant is open to the public at night and for Sunday brunch, banquets and catered events.

The extensive wine list, recipient of *The Wine Spectator's* Grand Award, features a cellar of 36,000 bottles. AVERAGE DINNER FOR TWO: $75

Menu Highlights

Appetizers

Pacific salmon tartare, brioche toast ∗ Poached tiger prawns with lobster mousse ∗ Warm spinach salad with mushrooms & pancetta

Entrées

Pacific abalone sautéed with lemon butter sauce ∗ Lamb Wellington with spinach & chestnut purée ∗ Broiled veal chop with morel mushroom sauce

DOROS

714 MONTGOMERY STREET
NEAR JACKSON
SAN FRANCISCO, CA 94111
(415) 397-6822

Major Credit Cards
Dinner Mon-Sat · Lunch Mon-Fri

Proprietor
Don Dianda

Chef
Paul Bermani

An important attraction of Doros is Don Dianda, its gracious and convivial owner and host. For over thirty years, Dianda has offered his guests dramatic decor and cuisine served with panache.

The small entryway opens into a large, brick-walled lounge area, decorated with eighteenth-century oil paintings. With well-lit red leather banquettes, the dining area is a showcase for food, wine and people.

Combining their skills for a quarter of a century, Dianda and Chef Paul Bermani have become a magical combination. Bermani prepares Continental entrées in the classical manner but goes beyond to also provide a memorable version of nouvelle cuisine.

The wine cellar boasts nearly 2,000 cases of treasured vintages. Not only has the Doros wine list repeatedly won *The Wine Spectator's* Grand Award, but it is also one of the very few American recipients of the International Award for having one of the best wine lists in the world.

AVERAGE DINNER FOR TWO: $80

Menu Highlights

A p p e t i z e r s

Crab legs on ice, mustard sauce ∗
Terrine of foie gras ∗ Crêpe stuffed
with Dungeness crab Delmonico ∗
Beluga caviar

E n t r é e s

Planked châteaubriand ∗ Veal
scalloppine à la Doros ∗ Noisette of
spring lamb sauté Cyrano ∗ Breast of
chicken à la Kiev ∗ Lobster tail & filet
mignon, mushroom caps & drawn butter

ERNIE'S

847 MONTGOMERY STREET
AT PACIFIC
SAN FRANCISCO, CA 94133
(415) 397-5969

Major Credit Cards
Open Daily · Dinner Only

Proprietors
Victor & Roland Gotti

Chef
Craig Thomas

In a city of restaurant legends, Ernie's is supreme. Proprietors Victor and Roland Gotti have guided their Victorian establishment to the pinnacle of the culinary industry.

What began in 1934 as a small Italian family eatery with linoleum floors and modestly set tables has grown into a showplace of elegant decor and French nouvelle cuisine that draws a clientele of the rich and famous. They recently undertook a major redecorating project, highlighting the fabulous Victorian architecture and furnishings of this award-winning restaurant. The Bacchus Wine Cellar, available for private parties, is a splendid old world setting with stone walls and massive wooden beams.

Ernie's wine selection is recognized as one of the finest in America and has received *The Wine Spectator's* Grand Award since its inception. Ernie's has also been a recipient of Mobil's Five Star Award for twenty-six consecutive years —an American record! AVERAGE DINNER FOR TWO: $80

Menu Highlights

Appetizers
Pâté en croute of duck, squab & quail, with mushroom & hazelnut oil hachis & jelly ∗ Baby rock lobster salad with an orange-truffle vinaigrette

Entrees
Very light lobster Bavarian with two sauces ∗ Braised oakleaf lettuce & fresh scallops in a fumé of cilantro & namekos mushrooms

HOUSE OF PRIME RIB

1906 VAN NESS AVENUE
NEAR JACKSON
SAN FRANCISCO, CA 94109
(415) 885-4605

Major Credit Cards
Open Daily · Dinner Only

Proprietor
Joe Betz

Chef
Salvador Rodriguez

The House of Prime Rib was a San Francisco institution, under the same management for thirty-seven years. Now it seems headed for another long and prosperous reign under proprietor Joe Betz.

In a complete remodeling, Betz decorated the interior with light, airy pastel colors and added brass-etched glass to recreate the atmosphere of an English pub. The specialty of the kitchen, however, has not changed. Each year at House of Prime Rib, some ninety tons of Eastern corn-fed beef are cured with a secret herb blend from England, packed in rock salt and roasted in seasoned ovens. The result: thick, juicy slices of prime rib, cooked to order and artfully carved from gleaming service carts at the table.

Chef Salvador Rodriguez, who has pre-sided in the kitchen here for many years, prepares each prime rib dinner and the accompaniments, as well as a fresh fish of the day. The pecan pie and other temptations from the dessert cart are worth the extra calories. AVERAGE DINNER FOR TWO: $45

Menu Highlights

Entrées

King Henry VIII cut of prime beef
∗ House of Prime Rib cut ∗ Prime rib à la carte ∗ Fresh fish: catch of the day ∗ All prime rib dinners served with salad, mashed or baked potatoes, Yorkshire pudding, creamed spinach and fresh horseradish sauce

LIVE A CUTTY ABOVE.

VICTOR'S

THE WESTIN ST. FRANCIS
335 POWELL STREET
SAN FRANCISCO, CA 94102
(415) 397-7000

Major Credit Cards
Dinner Daily · Sunday Brunch

Managing Director
Robert Wilhelm

Chef
Joel Rambaud

The award-winning Victor's, on the top floor of the prestigious Westin St. Francis Hotel, is a truly special find: a great hotel serving excellent food in a room with a spectacular view. After a breathtaking ride up thirty stories in an outside, glass-walled elevator, guests enter an elegant, wood-paneled corridor with recessed bookshelves housing leather-bound classics. In the dining room, floor-to-ceiling windows maximize the view of San Francisco and the Bay.

Chef Joel Rambaud, responding to the demands of his guests for California cuisine, has redefined a series of traditional recipes incorporating light sauces made to order with fresh produce from around the world. Dinner, before or after the theater, is enhanced by selections from a wine cellar that features more than 25,000 bottles.

Return for Sunday brunch at Victor's, a San Francisco tradition that draws a faithful local clientele. AVERAGE DINNER FOR TWO: $80

Menu Highlights

SEASONAL MENU

Appetizers

Chef Joel's duck foie gras ✴ Braised filet of baby salmon, dry vermouth & chive sauce ✴ Prawn & asparagus medley on roasted red pepper coulis

Entrées

Hot mesquite-smoked rack of lamb on bean ragout & sweet garlic sauce ✴ Veal medallions with wild Sierra mushrooms & essence of tarragon

The Elite Cafe

2049 FILLMORE STREET
AT CALIFORNIA
SAN FRANCISCO, CA 94115
(415) 346-8668

Major Credit Cards
Dinner Daily • Sunday Brunch

Proprietors
Tom Clendening &
Rahim Talai

Chef
Duane Mears

Any night of the week, a stylish crowd packs the bar at Elite Café, one of the more popular, vibrant dining spots in San Francisco. Dark polished wood trim runs the length of the dining room, adding to the Elite's New Orleans fishhouse atmosphere, and a lively crowd mingles at the oyster bar. For quiet dining, several private booths are set along the walls.

The Elite was the original Creole restaurant on the West Coast and helped popularize this American regional cuisine. Chef Duane Mears uses cast-iron pans to prepare blackened redfish fresh from the Pacific and blackened filet mignon. The soft-shell crabs, flown in from Chesapeake Bay, are a specialty, and the desserts are not to be missed.

Proprietors Tom Clendening and Rahim

Talai have created a signature restaurant that's both friendly and reliable. Their fine wine list specializes in California bottlings with an emphasis on whites. AVERAGE DINNER FOR TWO: $40

Menu Highlights

Appetizers
Oysters in Hell ∗ Creole gumbo ∗
Shrimp remoulade ∗ Fresh Louisiana
crawfish ∗ Spring salad

Entrées
Louisiana Chaurice sausage with red
beans & rice ∗ Stuffed creole eggplant ∗
Crab cakes ∗ Barbecued baby back ribs ∗
Blackened pork Louisiana

REGINA'S

REGIS HOTEL
490 GEARY STREET
SAN FRANCISCO, CA 94102
(415) 885-1661

Major Credit Cards
Dinner Tues-Sun · Lunch Tues-Fri · Sat & Sun Brunch

Proprietor
James Lunsford

Chef/Proprietor
Regina Charboneau

Of a handful of restaurants serving "Louisiana haute cuisine," Regina's has truly made a name for itself. Located on Theatre Row, the restaurant and convivial lounge are decorated with specially commissioned gold-framed sketches of performers who have graced the local theatre scene since the early 1900s. *Commedia* masks and colorful costume designs expand the thespian theme.

The leading lady in this dramatic setting is Regina Charboneau. Born in Natchez, Mississippi, just up the river from New Orleans, the La Varenne-trained chef has remained true to her French Creole roots, offering spicy yet sophisticated interpretations of New Orleans specialties.

Patrons flock to Regina's for the late-night "After the Arts" menu (served till 1AM on weekends). Offering everything from Southern cocktails to rich desserts, it is a perfect encore to an evening at the theatre. AVERAGE DINNER FOR TWO: $65

Menu Highlights

Appetizers

Peppered shrimp ∗ Fromage en croute ∗ Creole corn crab bisque ∗ Oysters 2, 2 & 2 (Bienville, Ohan & Rockefeller) ∗ Escargots sautéed with garlic, capers & sour cream

Entrées

Eggplant Lafayette with Gulf shrimp & crab ∗ Crawfish pie ∗ Lamb chops with tomato-mint marmalade ∗ Bouillabaisse ∗ Duck with seasoned rice dressing and fig preserves

JIL'S

242 O'FARRELL STREET
AT POWELL
SAN FRANCISCO, CA 94102
(415) 982-9353

Major Credit Cards
Closed Sunday · Lunch & Dinner

*Proprietors
Ilona & Jurgen Wondergem*

*Chef/Proprietor
Lucas Schoemaker*

It takes a lot of guts to transform a venerated French restaurant like Rene Verdon's Le Trianon into something casual, colorful and completely different. Three Dutch friends took on the challenge two years ago when they opened Jil's.

Jurgen and Ilona Wondergem and Lucas Schoemaker, all 26, named their restaurant after their first initials, changed the decor from stuffy red and gold to brazen blue, green and yellow, and set out to woo local diners with Lucas's eclectic European cuisine.

The restaurant's young attitude shines in such welcome experiments as a three-course lunch guaranteed to get you back to work in forty-five minutes and a pre-theatre menu for under $20 that allows guests to enjoy the appetizer and entrée before the show and return later for dessert and coffee.

Marked by intelligent experimentation and well-balanced flavors, Jil's cuisine appeals to a range of tastes and appetites, making this an ideal choice for group dining. AVERAGE DINNER FOR TWO: $50

Menu Highlights

SEASONAL MENU

Appetizers

Sweet curried oysters, cucumber sauce ∗ Grilled lamb sausage on greens with black olives ∗ Tuna carpaccio with tomato-cilantro vinaigrette

Entrées

Black pepper fetuccine with smoked salmon & chives ∗ Salmon Wellington, baked with herbs in filo dough ∗ Grilled veal chops with shiitake mushrooms

JULIUS' CASTLE

1541 MONTGOMERY STREET
NORTH OF UNION
SAN FRANCISCO, CA 94133
(415) 362-3042

Major Credit Cards
Dinner Daily · Lunch Mon-Fri

Manager
Jacques Kadik

Chef
Vidal Bitton

Built in 1921 by Julius Roz, Julius' Castle is one of San Francisco's most romantic dining experiences. Restaurateur Jeffrey Pollack has redesigned this San Francisco landmark to make the most of its location and heritage. One narrow staircase leads from the bar and reception area into the main dining room, another leads to the private rooms beneath the tower on the upper level.

From this restaurant on the cliffs of Telegraph Hill overlooking San Francisco Bay, every diner enjoys a stunning panorama—from Alcatraz to the Berkeley Hills and the expanse of bay in between. In the Victorian-style, wood-paneled main dining room, Gothic tables and Queen Anne chairs are all arranged to maximize the view.

Julius' Castle presents a contemporary European menu. The restaurant boasts a collection of rare scotch and cognac, along with an extensive wine list of fine old and new vintages, both local and imported.

AVERAGE DINNER FOR TWO: $70

Menu Highlights

SEASONAL MENU

Appetizers

Smoked Norwegian salmon filled with artichoke & truffle mousse * Fresh oysters in a flaky puff pastry shell with leeks & spinach, shallot-cream sauce

Entrées

Center-cut lamb chops stuffed with wild mushrooms, Cabernet-rosemary sauce * Sautéed scallops served with a truffle-enhanced mousse, pink peppercorn sauce

EUROPEAN

LASCAUX

248 SUTTER STREET
AT GRANT
SAN FRANCISCO, CA 94108
(415) 391-1555
Major Credit Cards
Closed Sunday • Lunch & Dinner

Proprietor
Annette Esser

Chef
Stephen Silva

The subterranean Lascaux, named after the cave in France containing some of the oldest drawings known to man, is as intriguing as its namesake. Created by renowned designer Pat Kuleto, its interior captures the feel of a real cave, with textured "stone" walls and arched ceilings, a hand-cut French limestone fireplace and alabaster wall sconces.

Deep, rich colors and soft lighting contribute a sense of elegance, while bas-relief reproductions of Lascaux's prehistoric cave paintings add an authentic touch. In this setting, Annette Esser has combined her appreciation for fine art with her love of European country cuisine.

"I was raised very much as a European," says Esser. "At Lascaux I wanted to recreate the homey, peasant-style taste-memories of my childhood." Chef Stephen Silva prepares unique dishes based on old European recipes in a menu celebrating the freshest offerings of the season.

AVERAGE DINNER FOR TWO: $50

Menu Highlights

SEASONAL MENU

Appetizers

House-cured gravlax with red onions, shallots & tarragon oil * Suppli: Italian mozzarella, prosciutto & rice croquette * Sundried tomato & basil torta of chevre & mascarpone.

Entrées

Braised rabbit with fresh tarragon & roasted garlic with potato pancake * Spit-roasted Provimi veal with Chardonnay sauce, Belgian endive & chives

ONE WORD CAPTURES THE MOMENT.
MUMM'S THE WORD.

Mumm Cordon Rouge. The only champagne to wear the red ribbon, symbol of France's highest honor.
To send a gift of Mumm Champagne, call 1-800-238-4373. Void where prohibited.

Inn At The Opera

Classically Designed Accommodations

Complete Guest Services

Specially Select Amenities

Personalized Attention to Detail

Cocktails & Dining in the Act IV Lounge

Romantic Weekend Packages

*A*n elegantly orchestrated hotel nestled among the day to evening excitement of San Francisco's Opera, Ballet, Symphony and dynamic Civic Center.

333 FULTON ST., SAN FRANCISCO, CA 94102 · 415-863-8400
Toll Free in CA 1-800/423-9610

F R E N C H

ACT IV

INN AT THE OPERA
333 FULTON STREET
SAN FRANCISCO, CA 94102
(415) 863-8400
Major Credit Cards
Open Daily · Lunch, Dinner & Late Supper

Maitre d'
Jack Jenkins

Chef
Christian Janselme

If you've dreamed of discovering here the kind of intimate yet sumptuous restaurant found in France's beautiful châteaux-inns, Act IV is your dream come true. As you walk through the Inn at the Opera's antique-filled sitting room and down a long hall lined with original 1874 Paul Renouard prints of scenes from the Paris Opéra, you are enveloped in the ambiance of a gracious private residence.

The dining room of Act IV, which has a cozy fireplace, is perfect for conversing and savoring the extraordinary cuisine of Chef Christian Janselme. With thirty years of experience in Nice and the prestige of having been a disciple of Auguste Escoffier, Janselme brings a fresh twist to French cuisine.

General Manager Annabella Wisniew-

ski says: "Christian can make the trendier light sauces, but his cooking has more flavor and intensity than nouvelle cuisine. And the portions are generous!" AVERAGE DINNER FOR TWO: $65

Menu Highlights

SEASONAL MENU

Appetizers

Poached oysters with Champagne sauce & caviar ∗ Fresh salmon in puff pastry with asparagus ∗ Selection of five caviars with five Champagnes

Entrées

Filet of rockfish with a touch of Provencal herbs ∗ Roast partridge stuffed with foie gras & truffles ∗ Filet of lamb with garlic basil & pinenuts

FRENCH

AMELIO'S

1630 POWELL STREET
NEAR GREEN
SAN FRANCISCO, CA 94133
(415) 397-4339
Major Credit Cards
Open Daily · Dinner Only

Proprietor
Chris Shearman

Chef/Proprietor
Jacky Robert

Established in 1926, Amelio's, long a favorite of San Franciscans, catapulted into culinary leadership in 1985, when it won the services of one of the most widely respected and emulated chefs in the United States, Jacky Robert.

With fourteen tables downstairs and banquet facilities for up to sixty guests upstairs, Proprietor Chris Shearman offers a choice of ambiance, from intimate to lively. A modest foyer belies the regal dining room just beyond the velvet curtain at Amelio's. Beautiful oil paintings and large mirrors in gilded frames enliven the dark wood-paneled walls. Impressive floral arrangements provide colorful accents throughout the softly lit dining area.

Amelio's is not the place for a quick, pre-theater meal; the meticulously pre-

pared menus are meant to be savored. As co-owner, Chef Robert has complete creative freedom, and his genius is blossoming. Amelio's menus showcase his unique presentation and finesse. AVERAGE DINNER FOR TWO: $80

Menu Highlights

SEASONAL MENU

Appetizers

Broiled marinated prawns ∗ Fresh foie gras sautéed with a raspberry vinegar sauce ∗ Woven pasta with shellfish

Entrées

Roast squab with star anise sauce & wild rice-saffron risotto ∗ Roast rack of lamb with transparent noodles, honey & soy sauce ∗ Young rabbit, sautéed, with greens & potato parasol, sesame glaze ∗ Fresh fish of the day

BRASSERIE CHAMBORD

152 KEARNY STREET
NEAR SUTTER
SAN FRANCISCO, CA 94104
(415) 434-3688

Major Credit Cards
Closed Sunday · Breakfast, Lunch & Dinner

Proprietors
Jean-Claude Lair
Giorgio Allegro & Jean Guinot

Chef
Alex J. Errecarte

Midway between San Francisco's financial district and the shopping mecca of Union Square, two Frenchmen and a Venetian have created an authentic and lively brasserie.

Owners Jean Guinot, Jean-Claude Lair and Giorgio Allegro opened this unique establishment in 1982. Any one of them—sometimes all three—can be found cutting fresh flowers, restocking the wine racks, inspecting the daily produce deliveries or looking over the skillfully presented plates leaving the kitchen. Such vigilantly maintained high standards keep a staunchly loyal clientele coming back.

"I love to research the traditional French recipes," says Chef Alex Errecarte, who is Basque in heritage, "and discover an overlooked herb or nuance that can give my customers more pleasure from my cooking."

Every two weeks, he changes his French regional specialties. A chalkboard lists French and California wines available by the glass. AVERAGE DINNER FOR TWO: $40

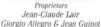
Menu Highlights

Appetizers
Housemade venison pâté * Escargots in a pastry shell * Baked clams with fine herbs & garlic * Calamari in su tinta

Entrées
Fish of the day * New York steak with five-peppercorn sauce * Provimi veal with mustard sauce * Grilled lamb chops with sauce diable * Baby lobster tails with tarragon sauce

CAFÉ MOZART

708 BUSH STREET
AT POWELL
SAN FRANCISCO, CA 94108
(415) 391-8480

Mastercard & Visa Only
Closed Monday · Dinner Only

Proprietor
Dr. Karl J. Kaussen

Chef
Thierry Quetelard

At Café Mozart proprietor Karl Kaussen has created a harmonic composition of decor and service, kitchen and dining room, food and wine.

The streetside picture windows are draped with red velvet and lace. Inside, ten tables are set with white china, etched crystal, baroque silver, candles in glass chimneys, white linen and roses in crystal vases. Antique clocks, seventeenth-century tapestries and Mozart cantatas complete what may be the most romantic restaurant setting in San Francisco.

In the kitchen, between two sideboards with beveled glass dividers, Chef Thierry Quetelard can be seen at work. The light *menu dégustation* shows concern for taste and calories; each course is a thoughtful blend of color, flavor and texture. The des-

sert plate of assorted sherbets, mousses and other sweets changes with the chef's whim.

Two private rooms, for parties of six to fourteen, provide intimacy for special occasions. AVERAGE DINNER FOR TWO: $90

Menu Highlights

Appetizers
Salmon mousse with red caviar ∗ Puff pastry shell with escargot clusters in red wine ∗ Blue Point oysters on a curry sauce of red peppers

Entrées
Rack of lamb with truffles & Sarladaise potatoes ∗ Boned breast of duck in cassis ∗ Medallions of veal with morel sauce ∗ Filet of salmon with basil sauce

evian.

de Ladoucette

Quite simply,
the ultimate Pouilly-Fumé

FLEUR DE LYS

777 SUTTER STREET
NEAR JONES
SAN FRANCISCO, CA 94109
(415) 673-7779

Major Credit Cards
Closed Sunday · Dinner Only

Proprietor
Maurice Rouas

Chef/Proprietor
Hubert Keller

Even though Fleur de Lys has had a devoted clientele since it opened in 1970, in 1986 Maurice Rouas decided to give his restaurant a shot in the arm. He did what many others before him had tried without success: he lured the talented Hubert Keller to Fleur de Lys as his new partner and chef.

Educated at the Hotel School in Strasbourg, France, Keller trained under such legendary chefs as Paul Haeberlin, Paul Bocuse, Gaston Lenotre and Roger Vergé. "I believe," he says, "in the sweetness of the onion, the green of the striped tigerella, the subtlety of the leek, the pervasiveness of the garlic and the intensity of Florence fennel."

The dramatic setting of Fleur de Lys suits Keller's cuisine, which, although steeped in classical tradition, welcomes the challenge of California's culinary revolution. Designed by the late Michael Taylor, the dining room is draped with hundreds of yards of hand-painted red floral fabric, like an immense garden tent.

AVERAGE DINNER FOR TWO: $100

Menu Highlights

SEASONAL MENU

Appetizers

American foie gras terrine, in fresh herb & black pepper gelée ∗ Thin-sliced Norwegian salmon in a tender corn pancake, with golden caviar, chive sauce

Entrées

Roasted lamb chops wrapped in vegetable mousseline, shallot-thyme red wine sauce ∗ Maine lobster on braised fennel with tomato, basil & virgin olive oil

JANOT'S

44 CAMPTON PLACE
AT UNION SQUARE
SAN FRANCISCO, CA 94108
(415) 392-5373
Major Credit Cards
Closed Sunday • Lunch & Dinner

Proprietor/Host
Jacques Janot

Chef/Proprietor
Pierre Morin

The epitome of Franco-California style, Janot's is a favorite downtown rendezvous by day and an upbeat dinner house by night. Brick walls, brass rails and dark green banquettes exude warmth and neatness, setting a perfect background for the polished cuisine of Chef/Owner Pierre Morin.

It may have seemed risky for Morin and his partner Jacques Janot to open a French restaurant when California cuisine was the talk of the town. But these two veterans of the San Francisco restaurant business knew exactly what they were doing. Using French techniques, a very quick cooking style and a fresh approach inspired by California's agricultural plenitude, they created an ideal French-American blend.

Three years later, critics from every major publication, from *Gourmet* and *Esquire* to the *San Francisco Chronicle* and the *New York Times,* were unanimous: Janot's impeccable look and superb light fare were just what San Francisco needed. AVERAGE DINNER FOR TWO: $50

Menu Highlights

Appetizers

Seafood sausage with warm cabbage salad
* Grilled quail with smoked bacon & spinach salad

Entrées

Breast of chicken with horseradish sauce & chives * Rolled filet of sole stuffed with spinach & tarragon, white butter sauce * Prawns, scallops & oysters molded in cabbage leaves, fennel butter sauce

FRENCH

LA FOLIE

2316 POLK STREET
AT GREEN
SAN FRANCISCO, CA 94109
(415) 776-5577

Mastercard & Visa Only
Closed Sunday • Dinner Only

Maître d'
Georges Passot
Proprietor
Jamie Passot

Chef/Proprietor
Roland Passot

Since La Folie opened last spring, San Francisco's best chefs and restaurateurs have been spending their nights off sampling Roland Passot's creations. Roland's talent for strong, flavorful cuisine matched by bold presentations was known from his days at Le Francais in Chicago, San Francisco's now-closed Chez Michel, and the top restaurants of Lyons, France.

"I call my cooking spontaneous," says the genial Roland. "I never know what I'm going to prepare until after I call my suppliers."

The dining room, with its clouds painted on a blue ceiling and monkeys and parrots cavorting on yellow drapes, is crazy enough to convey the "folly" implied by the restaurant's name, yet as warm and inviting as a family-run restaurant should be. Roland's wife, Jamie, is the friendly hostess. Brother Georges, the maitre d' and sommelier, has assembled a unique wine list featuring outstanding, little-known French and California selections at great prices. AVERAGE DINNER FOR TWO: $75

Menu Highlights

SEASONAL MENU

Appetizers

Warm potato terrine with foie gras & smoked duck, hazelnut vinaigrette * Ravioli of sea scallops & shiitake mushrooms wrapped in cabbage, citrus butter & chives

Entrées

Roast sturgeon with Banuyls sauce & a leek infusion, served with bone marrow flan * Sliced breast of duck with Calvados sauce, served with apples & pinenuts

LE CENTRAL

453 BUSH STREET
AT GRANT
SAN FRANCISCO, CA 94108
(415) 391-2233

Major Credit Cards
Closed Sunday · Lunch & Dinner

Proprietor
Claude Cappelle

Chef
Paul Tanphanich

Fifteen years ago, when brothers Claude and Pierre Cappelle opened Le Central, the first authentic French brasserie in San Francisco, they imbued it with such gaiety and style, such heart-warming food, that they had no rivals. "Every item on the menu was something that wasn't being served in any local French restaurant," recalls Claude Cappelle.

Day and night, The City's elite jostled for tables in the narrow, lively dining rooms of Le Central. But then, alas, the charismatic Cappelles left, and the warmth and tradition they had created left with them.

Today, the brothers are back. They are again filling this intimate, brick-walled brasserie—so typically French with its mirrors, its handwritten black-board menus and its famous regional dishes—with the inimitable casual ambiance that can evoke Paris in a plate of cassoulet. The classically hearty dishes are still there, but you'll also find lighter California-style entrées. AVERAGE DINNER FOR TWO: $50

Menu Highlights

Appetizers

Fresh celery root remoulade ∗ Crab cake beurre blanc ∗ Warm garlic sausage, potatoes & vinaigrette

Entrées

Paillard of chicken with pasta ∗ Grilled duck sausage with polenta ∗Grilled red snapper with eggplant & tomato, olive sauce ∗ Cold salmon sauce verte

FRENCH

LE PIANO ZINC

708 14TH STREET
AT MARKET
SAN FRANCISCO, CA 94114
(415) 431-5266
Major Credit Cards
Closed Monday · Dinner Only

Proprietor
Joel Coutre

Chef/Proprietor
Michel Laurent

If you're looking for a restaurant where you'll feel at ease right away, Le Piano Zinc will seduce you. Music from a white baby grand, sometimes accompanied by an American chanteuse, fills this intimate brasserie late into the night. Regulars abound, the small bar is packed, and the food is so good that diners can't resist passing plates around the table.

When they opened Le Piano Zinc two and a half years ago, Joel Coutre and Michel Laurent envisioned a simple brasserie menu. Instead, they reintroduced authentic French cuisine as good as that of any three-star restaurant in France.

Laurent is an accomplished chef who makes everything from the sausages to the sorbets from scratch. He offers a dozen appetizers and as many entrées, a prix-fixe menu that changes every day, and up to fifteen desserts. Somewhere between Coutre's friendly welcome, the foie gras and the crème brulée, you'll fall in love with Le Piano Zinc. AVERAGE DINNER FOR TWO: $70

Menu Highlights

SEASONAL MENU
Appetizers
Medallion of salmon between shiitake mushroom caps, chive sauce ✳ Terrine of fresh foie gras & Maine lobster with leeks & tomatoes

Entrées
Steamed filet of John Dory with old-fashioned Pommery mustard sauce & tomato coulis ✳ Chicken supreme sautéed with chanterelle mushrooms, cream of pistou

L'ÉTOILE

1075 CALIFORNIA STREET
NEAR TAYLOR
SAN FRANCISCO, CA 94108
(415) 771-1529

Major Credit Cards
Closed Sunday • Dinner Only

☎ 🍸 🚗 🍴 🅥 🎵 PR

Proprietors
Henri Barberis &
Claude Rouas

Chef
Claude Bougard

L'Etoile has the style of the great restaurants of New York City from the late '50s and early '60s. The reception room has a gracious serenity that makes the pressures of the outside world vanish. A staircase leads down to the French African-style lounge and bar, decorated with leopard skin-covered throw pillows and mounted hunting trophies on the wall.

At the piano, Peter Mintun's stylish playing sets a tone of wry sophistication that draws many of The City's most notable people. Proprietors Claude Rouas and Henri Barberis have recreated the quiet luxury of Maxim's in Paris and Le Pavillon in New York in the dining room designed by Michael Taylor.

Claude Bougard, L'Etoile's chef for sixteen years, completes this circle of stylish dining. Chef Bougard, trained in classic cuisine, has now embraced some of the concepts of nouvelle cuisine. The wine list offers choices from a fine California collection and an extraordinary French cellar. AVERAGE DINNER FOR TWO: $95

Menu Highlights

Appetizers

Assorted salad with quail, goose liver pâté & lobster ∗ Warm French green beans with Bay scallops ∗ Salmon scallops with herb butter & caviar

Entrées

Filet of sole & oysters with Champagne sauce ∗ Chicken in raspberry vinegar sauce ∗ Squab with armagnac sauce & liver pâté

BOLLINGER

D. CHAMPAGNE

MAKE A SCENE

La Nouvelle Patisserie
is not an average
French pastry shop.
Chef Jean-Yves Duperret
has brought to
San Francisco
the best French
pastries and cakes.

*Also featured
at Neiman-Marcus
Ice Cream Cakes
for Summer
Fancy Chocolates
for any
Special Occasion*

OPEN EVERY DAY

2184 Union Street
San Francisco
415/931-7655

JEAN-YVES DUPERRET, *Maitre Patiss*

LA NOUVEL
PATISSERI

FRENCH

L'OLIVIER

465 DAVIS STREET
NEAR JACKSON
SAN FRANCISCO, CA 94111
(415) 981-7824
Major Credit Cards
Dinner Mon-Sat · Lunch Mon-Fri

Proprietors
Christian & Guy Francoz

Chef
Eric Branger

L'Olivier is a popular business-lunch place for executives by day and a romantic dining spot by night. As soon as one enters through the large solarium filled with greenery and fresh flowers, one senses the relaxing, sensuous and elegant ambiance. The main dining room, decorated with a French provincial fabric and French antiques, has a quiet and inviting atmosphere.

Proprietors Christian and Guy Francoz offer a traditional French menu, with adroit and pleasant service from a young staff. Chef Eric Branger, recently arrived from Florida, trained for three years with Paul Bocuse in France. He continues L'Olivier's culinary tradition of recipes that are classical, yet light and low in calories. As always, the desserts are superbly rich.

Featuring the most current California selections as well as renowned French vintages, the wine list is a pleasure to peruse. AVERAGE DINNER FOR TWO: $55

Menu Highlights

Appetizers
Frog legs soup * Marble of goose liver *
Seafood sausage in a lobster sauce *
Feuillete of lobster & spinach

Entrées
Roast salmon medallions with confit ginger
& wild mushrooms * Stuffed breast of
chicken with vegetables & truffles *
Boneless squab with shiitake mushrooms
& apple vinegar sauce

FRENCH

MASA'S

648 BUSH STREET
NEAR STOCKTON
SAN FRANCISCO, CA 94108
(415) 989-7154

Major Credit Cards
Closed Sunday & Monday · Dinner Only

Manager
Nick Peyton

Chef
Julian Serrano

The memory of master chef Masataki Kobayashi guides Chef Julian Serrano as he carries on the visual and gastronomic artistry at Masa's. Together with Maitre d' Nick Peyton and owner Bill Kimpton, Serrano has maintained the impeccable standards set by both Masa and his successor William Galloway. Trained in Madrid, Serrano worked with Masa for three years: "I express myself within the unique style and tradition he set."

The magic at Masa's is a combination of aesthetic flair and outstanding cooking; there is so much on each plate, so carefully presented, that it takes at least six steps and sixteen people in the kitchen to create an entrée.

The wine list is outstanding, and a modest wine bar serves an extensive Californian and French selection. Where else could you find Château d'Yquem by the glass? AVERAGE DINNER FOR TWO: $130

Menu Highlights

Appetizers

Sausage of lobster, scallop & shrimp with fresh herbs ∗ Poached oysters with vermouth sauce & Serruga caviar ∗ Fresh sautéed foie gras with truffles & spinach

Entrées

Grilled Maine lobster with herb beurre blanc & shrimp quenelles ∗ Roast breast of pheasant with morels & marinated pears ∗ Grilled filet of lamb with green peppercorns, sauce Zinfandel

Food & Beverage Director
Gerard Hotelier

Chef
Sebastien Urbain

PIERRE AT MERIDIEN

HOTEL MERIDIEN
50 THIRD STREET
SAN FRANCISCO, CA 94103
(415) 974-6400

Major Credit Cards
Closed Monday · Dinner Only

FRENCH

When Pierre opened in the Hotel Meridien in 1983, it immediately attracted a following among both City residents and visitors. Conveniently located near Union Square, the Meridien is one of San Francisco's foremost hotels.

Pierre has a genuine French formality without pretentiousness, presenting gracious and professional service, hand-painted porcelain dinnerware, sparkling crystal glassware and fresh flowers to complement the sumptuous menu.

Chef Sebastien Urbain achieves a unique balance between classic French and inventive California cuisine. A prix-fixe tasting menu is presented nightly, and several times a year one of France's culinary superstars prepares a series of special dinners as part of Pierre's popular

Master Chefs of France program. The expertly researched wine list offers a fine selection of both French and California wines. AVERAGE DINNER FOR TWO: $85

Menu Highlights

SEASONAL MENU

Appetizers

Warm sea scallops with fresh tomatoes & dill
∗ Salad of sautéed fresh foie gras & Maine
lobster ∗ Puff pastry with Petaluma snails &
shrimp with sorrel-Riesling butter

Entrées

Poached sea bass with caviar & green
asparagus tips ∗ Fresh monkfish with sweet
garlic & eggplant flan ∗ Filet of veal with
tagliolini pasta

THE PORTMAN GRILL

THE PORTMAN
500 POST STREET
SAN FRANCISCO, CA 94102
(415) 771-8600

Major Credit Cards
Open Daily · Breakfast, Lunch & Dinner

Managing Director
Patrick Mene

Chef
Fred Halpert

Set in the tan marble lobby of The Portman, The Grill conveys a friendly, informal atmosphere. It's the perfect match for Chef Fred Halpert's casual yet elegant cuisine based on the robust flavors of Provence.

The outgoing Halpert decided to become a chef after he had already earned a degree in finance. He trained with the best chefs in France, including Alain Chapel, Roger Vergé and Alain Senderens, dodging immigration officials who wanted to send him home. After almost four years, he returned to the United States, where he made a name for himself in Los Angeles at Mangia, then in San Francisco at Restaurant 101.

The Grill is a very relaxing place to go before or after the theatre, with well-priced prix-fixe menus that include excellent wines. Chef Halpert is especially proud of his pasta dishes, and has a passion for fresh vegetables and herbs. Like its creator, the cuisine here is dynamic, honest and original. AVERAGE DINNER FOR TWO: $80

Menu Highlights

SEASONAL MENU

Appetizers

Salad of sautéed American duck liver with artichokes & basil * Angel hair pasta with sea scallops, onions & thyme

Entrées

Sautéed Pacific salmon with olive oil & fresh herbs * Sautéed Santa Barbara prawns with Pommery mustard sauce * Sautéed Muscovy duck breast with artichokes & thyme

THE ART OF
LA MARCA

THE ART OF
SÁFILO

THE ART OF
MANFREDI

THE ART OF
ALESSI

PART OF THE ART.

𝕱rangelico®
liqueur

The delicate hazelnut liqueur from Italy.

To send a gift of Frangelico anywhere in the U.S. call 1-800-238-4373.

Void where prohibited by law. 28% Alc/Vol (56 Proof). Produced and bottled by Barbero S.P.A., Canale, Italy. Imported by William Grant & Sons, Inc., N.Y., N.Y.

THE SHERMAN HOUSE
...there is only one in the world.

A hotel, as intimate and luxurious as the grandest of homes. Hours of enchantment can pass as you lounge in one of our fifteen rooms or suites, nestled in a quiet nook overlooking the Golden Gate Bridge, while a wood-burning fireplace warms your thoughts. Or you may wish to quietly sit in the three-story music room, where Jan Paderewski once shared court with other musical notables.

You will find comfort in knowing that our chef awaits your every whim . . . you may dine in our restaurant or simply enjoy the luxury of twenty-four hour room service. This historical landmark hotel in Pacific Heights offers all that you wish you did not have to leave at home. . . .

2160 Green Street, San Francisco, CA 94123, (415) 563-3600, Telex: 383322

SHERMAN HOUSE

2160 GREEN STREET
NEAR FILLMORE
SAN FRANCISCO, CA 94123
(415) 563-3600

Major Credit Cards
Open Daily to Hotel Guests for Lunch & Dinner

Proprietors
Vesta & Manou Mobedshahi

Chef
Neal Langermann

The Sherman House, a historical landmark dating back to 1876, was the private mansion of Leander Sherman, founder of Sherman Clay Music Co. Under the meticulous guidance of Manou Mobedshahi, the house was converted into a small luxury hotel, with carriage house and formal gardens, and features eighteenth-century-inspired interiors recreated by the late premier designer Billy Gaylord.

Chef Neal Langermann, a newcomer to the Sherman House kitchen, continues the tradition of fine cuisine with an emphasis on creativity and detailed presentation. He makes each dish a hallmark of excellence, especially the *menu gastronomique,* $60, and *menu dégustation,* $75.

For special events and private parties,

the spendid chandeliered three-storied Music Room, with its third-floor Gallery Salon, may accommodate forty-five for gracious dining, or eighty for beautifully orchestrated receptions. AVERAGE DINNER FOR TWO: $120

Menu Highlights

A SAMPLE MENU GASTRONOMIQUE

* Délice du Roi
* Sabayon d'homard
* Saint-Jacques á la citronette
* Perrier Jouet sorbet
* Selle d'agneau à la menthe
* Salade vinaigrette de truffes
* Fromage St. Honoré
* Picasso petits fours

Proprietor
Larry Bain

Chef/Proprietor
Catherine Pantsios
Chef
Rachel Gardner

ZOLA'S

FRENCH

1722 SACRAMENTO STREET
AT VAN NESS
SAN FRANCISCO, CA 94109
(415) 775-3311

Major Credit Cards
Closed Sunday & Monday • Dinner Only

With Larry Bain up front and wife Catherine Pantsios in the kitchen, Zola's has such a personal feeling it's no wonder so many of its clients are regulars. The two, who met in New York where she was a chef at The Quilted Giraffe and he was at The Odeon, have created a friendly intimacy that is as genuine as the French country-style cuisine they serve.

"Catherine and Rachel like food that is nourishing and comforting," says Bain. "They believe in traditional cooking methods that require heat and time to create deep, complex flavors."

The chefs excel at cassoulets, confits and such dishes as braised oxtails, which are defatted, deboned and wrapped in cabbage leaves.

A constant favorite of local and national food critics, Zola's enters its sixth year with the same moderate prices and unpretentious ambiance that have made it so popular. AVERAGE DINNER FOR TWO: $55

Menu Highlights

MONTHLY MENU

Appetizers

Fresh tomato & herb tart ✳ Salad of roast squab with lentils & pickled beets ✳ Sautéed sweetbread salad with orange-hazelnut dressing

Entrées

Roast breast & braised leg of duck with red grapes ✳ Seared tuna with mustard beurre blanc ✳ Cassoulet with pork, chicken & sausage

INTERNATIONAL

SQUARE ONE

190 PACIFIC AVENUE
NEAR FRONT
SAN FRANCISCO, CA 94111
(415) 788-1110

Major Credit Cards
Open Daily for Dinner · Lunch Mon-Fri

Proprietor
Evan Goldstein

Chef/Proprietor
Joyce Goldstein

"Square One is in love with food," says Joyce Goldstein, who directs the daily preparations in her immaculate kitchens. Her restaurant—modernistic, clean-cut, with large windows looking onto Sidney Walton Park—has a light, airy, outdoor feeling.

The name Square One implies a fresh beginning every day, and recreating the classics while developing new recipes is one of the two obsessions that prevail here. Each day, Square One presents an international repertoire with many Mediterranean recipes. The menu also makes forays into Latin America, India, the Orient and the United States.

"I treat my restaurant like my home," Goldstein says. "I don't like to cook or eat the same things every night. So diversity is my fare." Goldstein's oenophile son

Evan, 26, last year became the youngest American to gain membership in the prestigious British Master Court of Sommeliers. AVERAGE DINNER FOR TWO: $65

Menu Highlights

DAILY MENU

Appetizers

Avocado with gazpacho vinaigrette ∗ Baked goat cheese with arugula, green beans & sundried tomato vinaigrette

Entrees

Paella: saffron rice with lobster, Manila clams, chorizo, chicken, artichokes, onions, tomatoes & peppers ∗ Roast duck orientale with ginger, honey, lemon, orange, hot pepper & Chinese five spices

INTERNATIONAL

TRADER VIC'S

20 COSMO PLACE
NEAR TAYLOR
SAN FRANCISCO, CA 94108
(415) 776-2232

Major Credit Cards
Open Daily • Lunch & Dinner

Proprietor
Lynn Bergeron

Chef
Klaus Selb

The late Victor Bergeron created a worldwide dining empire based on exotic fare in equally exotic settings. His first wife dubbed him Trader Vic, for his habit of trading goods for services. At his namesake restaurant in San Francisco, the elite of The City, European royalty and an international jet set vie for access to the Captain's Cabin, one of the most exclusive dining rooms in the Bay Area.

"I never bought a cheap chicken," The Trader used to say. This is still the guideline for Lynn Bergeron, Vic's son and the restaurant proprietor. The cuisine is a mélange of Chinese, Polynesian and Indian, and much of it is prepared in two huge ovens visible through a large window at the entry.

The famous tropical drinks use three or more types of rum, fresh fruit and Trader Vic's patented syrup mixes. The list includes Gun Club Punch, Navy Grog and M'ai T'ai. In Tahitian, *M'ai t'ai* means "the very best," and that is Trader Vic's.

AVERAGE DINNER FOR TWO: $70

Menu Highlights

Appetizers

Tahitian crab cocktail ∗ Prawns mimosa ∗ Artichoke soup ∗ Barbecued spare ribs ∗ Trader Vic's tidbits: fried prawns, spare ribs, crab Rangoon, sliced pork

Entrées

Lobster flambé Trader Vic style ∗ Indonesian lamb roast from a Chinese oven ∗ Barbecued double pork loin with pineapple & chutney

TRY A LITTLE WISHFUL DRINKING.

Legend has it that
if you add three
coffee beans to
Sambuca Romana,
good fortune will follow.

THE LEGENDARY LIQUEUR
OF GOOD FORTUNE.

MOLTO
CERETTO

*STILE
QUALITÀ
MODERNO
ITALIANO*

CERETTO
Produce ed affina vini del Piemonte in Alba

RESCO
Denominazione di origine controllata
e garantita

Registro imbott. 8671 CN - Imbott.

THE BLUE FOX

659 MERCHANT STREET
AT MONTGOMERY
SAN FRANCISCO, CA 94111
(415) 981-1117
Major Credit Cards
Closed Sunday • Dinner Only

Proprietor
Gianni Fassio

Chef
Patrizio Sacchetto

At the peak of his career as an accountant, Gianni Fassio bought the Blue Fox. "Mario Mondin asked me to find him a buyer," says Fassio, whose father had been Mondin's partner. "I counted fifteen seconds and said, 'You've found him.'"

Fassio grew up working in the Blue Fox and had dreamed of making it a Milan-style Italian restaurant. First, he found his ideal chef, Patrizio Sacchetto, who had cooked at the famous Rex, Il Ristorante in Los Angeles and taught at the California Culinary Academy. Sacchetto chose to recreate La Cucina Nobile Italiana, the aristocratic cuisine of sixteenth- and seventeenth-century Italy.

Then Fassio and his wife refurbished the fifty-five-year-old restaurant. In May, 1988, a bright, new Blue Fox opened.

Only one feature remains unchanged: the two fantastic private rooms in the cellar, where generations of San Franciscans have celebrated their special occasions.

AVERAGE DINNER FOR TWO: $90

Menu Highlights

SEASONAL MENU

Appetizers

Venison carpaccio with essence of white truffle * Quail risotto * Gnocchi, gorgonzola cheese sauce * Rainbow pappardelle, basil butter sauce

Entrées

Veal loin with sautéed asparagus tips * Sautéed sea bass wrapped in potatoes, meunière sauce * Rack of lamb wrapped in a vegetable mousseline, Madeira sauce

BUCA GIOVANNI

800 GREENWICH STREET
NEAR COLUMBUS
SAN FRANCISCO, CA 94133
(415) 776-7766

Major Credit Cards
Closed Sunday · Dinner Only

Maitre d'
Cesare Di Lorenzo

Chefs/Proprietors
Giovanni Leoni & David Siering

True to its name, Giovanni's "cave" is a romantic brick-walled retreat down a short flight of stairs. The real action, however, is in the open kitchen upstairs, where those seated at the few small tables can watch Giovanni Leoni and partner/chef David Siering prepare their Tuscan specialties.

Leoni, who was chef at Vanessi's for eighteen years before opening his restaurant five years ago, directs every aspect of Buca Giovanni. Up at dawn, he does the daily marketing, and on Sundays, returns from a visit to his family ranch in Ukiah with dozens of fresh rabbits in the back of his car. Leoni grows his own herbs, lettuce and tomatoes, and will search for years to find the best ricotta or the best coffee beans (which he then roasts him-

self on the premises).

His exacting standards can be tasted in every preparation, from the earthy salsa rosa, an addictive purée of sundried tomatoes, anchovies, garlic, capers and vinegar, to the ethereal ricotta gnocchi.

AVERAGE DINNER FOR TWO: $50

Menu Highlights

Appetizers

Warm rabbit salad from our ranch with radicchio * Antipasto misto la Buca * Round raviolini stuffed with eggplant & gorgonzola in a basil sauce

Entrées

Rabbit with grappa * Venison with wild fennel * Roasted scampi wrapped in prosciutto * Lamb stuffed with mortadella, herbs, porcini mushrooms & wrapped in grape leaves

ITALIAN

DONATELLO

501 POST STREET
AT MASON
SAN FRANCISCO, CA 94102
(415) 441-7182
Major Credit Cards
Open Daily · Lunch & Dinner

Proprietor
A. Cal Rossi, Jr.

Chef
Suzette Gresham

Donatello is the leader of a growing cluster of Italian restaurants in Northern California taking a serious look at fine Italian cuisine. Located near Union Square in the elegant Donatello Hotel, the restaurant was named for a leading Italian Renaissance sculptor. Donatello's two dining rooms are distinctively decorated with Venetian glass, marble, Carpaccio lamps, Fortuny fabric panels and an abundance of mirrors.

Creator and owner A. Cal Rossi took an early and active role in shaping Donatello's style and standards. This personal involvement carries over into the flawless preparation and presentation of Chef Suzette Gresham.

Donatello also invites the most renowned chefs of Italy to preside in its kitchen for one week each year, giving the staff a rare opportunity to keep abreast of the latest in Italian cooking. Another attraction is its four-course gastronomic menu ($65) that offers a bottomless pouring of three different wines. AVERAGE DINNER FOR TWO: $80

Menu Highlights

A p p e t i z e r s
Smoked sturgeon & baby field lettuce with olive oil & lemon ∗ Artichokes & prawns fricassée with basil ∗Gratinéed cream of borlotti beans & barley

E n t r é e s
Fresh poached lobster in a sweet red pepper purée ∗Medallions of venison with wild mushrooms ∗Veal chop in a Madeira sauce with fresh rosemary

MODESTO LANZONE'S

601 VAN NESS AVENUE
AT OPERA PLAZA
SAN FRANCISCO, CA 94102
(415) 928-0400

Major Credit Cards
Dinner Mon-Sat · Lunch Mon-Fri

Proprietor
Modesto Lanzone

Chef
Mathew Cook

In 1980, music and art benefactor Modesto Lanzone decided to build a restaurant around his famed art collection and locate it near the cultural center of San Francisco. A whimsical bust of Modesto by Robert Arneson —a string of pasta here, a bit of tomato sauce there—smilingly greets guests at the entrance.

The interior, by Teresa Pomodoro, designer of the new San Francisco Museo Italo-Americano, places each art piece as a highlight of the plan. From Milan to Kyoto, the world's finest artistic tradition and innovation are represented here, but with Lanzone's imprint. "I listen only to my own madness," he says.

This setting of artistry with an undercurrent of drama is echoed in the Northern Italian cuisine—classic cooking with innovative seasoning and meticulous attention to quality. The pasta is made fresh daily by Lanzone's sisters. The superb wine list features Italian selections, as well as choices from France and California. AVERAGE DINNER FOR TWO: $70

Menu Highlights

Appetizers

Prosciutto & melon ∗ Mozzarella with tomatoes & basil ∗ Slices of rabbit with endive ∗ Poached veal in tuna sauce

Entrées

Prawns sautéed with garlic & tomatoes ∗ Lamb double loin marinated in herbs ∗ Chicken with artichoke hearts, mushrooms & sour cream ∗ Cannelloni alla Rossini stuffed with veal, cheese & vegetables

ITALIAN

RAF

478 GREEN STREET
AT GRANT
SAN FRANCISCO, CA 94133
(415) 362-1999

Major Credit Cards
Open Daily for Dinner · Lunch Mon-Fri
Sat & Sun Brunch

Manager
George Milliken

Executive Chef
Rick O'Connell

When it comes to Italian cuisine, RAF Centrogriglia's Rick O'Connell is a stickler for what belongs and what doesn't. "Putting garlic in a dish that doesn't call for it is like putting your jacket on backwards," she says.

O'Connell's parents were born in Italy and raised her on good Italian cooking. "It's in my blood." Her exciting, modern versions of regional Italian dishes have received nationwide accolades.

Another attention-getter is RAF's decor. "People keep asking me when we're going to finish it," laughs manager George Milliken. Designed by Amy McGill, RAF has exposed roof beams, faux tree branches and unbaked clay formed into floral wreaths around huge mirrors, which add to its humorous charm. Says Milliken, "It looks like a Tuscan villa — after the war."

On warm days, patrons can enjoy lunch outdoors in RAF's sunny garden. AVERAGE DINNER FOR TWO: $70

Menu Highlights

Appetizers

Antipasto for two ✳ Carpaccio with capers, roasted garlic & parmesan ✳ Risotto balls ✳ Minestrone ✳ Clams in brodo

Entrées

Risotto Milanese ✳ Pasta carbonara ✳ Grilled lamb chops marinated & sauced with pomegranate ✳ Prawn & squid sauté with sopressata ✳ Quail with polenta & sausage pie

Director
S. Fujimoto

Chef
K. Koide

BENKAY

HOTEL NIKKO
222 MASON STREET
SAN FRANCISCO, CA 94102
(415) 394-1111

Major Credit Cards
Open Daily for Dinner · Breakfast & Lunch Mon-Fri

RISING STAR

JAPANESE

Stepping off the elevator on the twenty-fifth floor of the Hotel Nikko, you enter a world so serene that stress falls away with each step across the silver-grey carpet. With its intimate waiting areas, meditational rock gardens and large windows framing the city's skyline, Benkay is a beautiful setting for Kaiseki, a cuisine derived from the Japanese tea ceremony.

Unfamiliar even to some Japanese, Kaiseki consists of a succession of many exquisite courses composed to harmonize taste, color and texture. The service by kimono-clad waitresses obeys tradition, as does the presentation on imported porcelain and lacquer dishes, each specific to a course.

In addition to Kaiseki, Benkay offers a menu of à la carte dishes in its sleek, contemporary dining room. To experience the full pleasure of Kaiseki, however, you'll want to reserve one of Benkay's six private tatami rooms. AVERAGE DINNER FOR TWO: $90

Menu Highlights

Dinners

Shizuka Kaiseki: appetizers, sashimi, soup, simmered vegetables, skewered-grilled dish, deep-fried dish, Japanese salad, rice, miso soup, pickled vegetables ✳ Tokiwaka Kaiseki: deluxe ten-course dinner of fish, fowl, meat & vegetables ✳ Tempura Kaiseki: appetizers, sashimi, simmered vegetables, prawn, fish & vegetable tempura, salad, rice, miso soup, dessert ✳ Shabu-shabu ✳ Yosenabe

YOSHIDA-YA

2909 WEBSTER STREET
AT UNION
SAN FRANCISCO, CA 94123
(415) 346-3431

Major Credit Cards
Open Daily • Dinner Only

General Manager
Kenny Makino

Chef
Ken Saito

The inviting interior of Yoshida-Ya hints at the traditional ambiance to be found within. Touches of Kyoto red and shades of apricot appear throughout the serene wooden and tile interior. The ground floor has been remodeled so that one section serves sixty kinds of appetizers—sushi, yakitori grilled chicken, meat and vegetables, and lots of other tantalizing Japanese tidbits. It's an informal, modern way to dine. Upstairs, relax at regular tables, or sit on the floor at low tables over wells, which allow for Western-style comfort.

Chef Ken Saito, a master of traditional Japanese cooking, prepares the famous Omakase "leave it to the chef" dinner with two days' advance notice. It is Japanese cuisine, both traditional and original, some of which is influenced by the cuisine of other countries.

Several times a year, Yoshida-Ya invites the best chefs of Japan to prepare gala dinners on Japanese themes. Don't miss them! AVERAGE DINNER FOR TWO: $50

Menu Highlights

Appetizers

Four varieties of mushrooms sautéed in sake-butter sauce ∗ Caviar ginger tofu: tofu served cold with flying-fish eggs & ginger soy sauce ∗ Sushi

Entrées

Filet mignon hibachi ∗ Grilled mustard chicken roll ∗ Yellow tail teriyaki ∗ Broiled eel with special sauce ∗ Assorted sashimi

VIETNAMESE

GOLDEN TURTLE

2211 VAN NESS AVENUE
AT BROADWAY
SAN FRANCISCO, CA 94109
(415) 441-4419

Major Credit Cards
Closed Monday · Lunch & Dinner

Proprietors
Kim-Quy Tran
Kham Dinh Tran

Chef/Proprietor
Kim-Quy Tran

In the sixth century, A.D., a mythical golden turtle helped win the war for Vietnamese independence from China by rising up out of Hoang-Kiem Lake and giving a young general a mighty sword. As a result, the turtle became a respected figure in Vietnamese culture. Good fortune is said to follow those named for the golden turtle.

One of the fortunate ones is Kim-Quy Tran, who with her husband Kham opened the first Golden Turtle on the corner of 5th Avenue and Clement Street in 1977. Over the years, the Golden Turtle grew so popular that the location became too small. So the Trans opened a second, more opulent restaurant on Van Ness in 1986.

The Golden Turtle is that rarity of rarities, a restaurant that has never had an unfavorable review — with good reason.

Chef Tran's cuisine is the embodiment of the finest Vietnamese cooking. AVERAGE DINNER FOR TWO: $40

Menu Highlights

Appetizers
Imperial rolls * Shrimp & pork salad *
Marinated barbecued quail * Charbroiled
shrimp sticks with fresh vegetables,
noodles & plum sauce

Entrées
Seven jewel beef dinner * Pan-fried crab
with ginger & garlic sauce * Lemon grass
chicken with hot chiles * Tender "luc lac"
beef with salad & Vietnamese dressing *
Special banquet dinner for four or more

WELL, THE GLENLIVET Scotch whisky does cost around $20.00. Which some say is a small price to pay for a Scotch which has been made in the same unique way since 1747. A 12-year-old single malt Scotch with a smoothness and unique character that is unsurpassed to this day. All of which could explain why people are so strangely possessive about The Glenlivet. Which is a pity. You might just have to buy a bottle of your own.

THE GLENLIVET® JUST SLIGHTLY OUT OF REACH

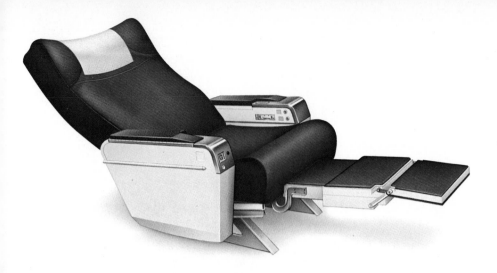

If You Think All Airline Seats Are The Same, Sit In This One For 6,000 Miles.

On UTA French Airlines to Paris when you buy an airline ticket, you're buying much more than just an airline seat.

Over 50 years of experience flying the world's longest and most exotic routes has taught us it's the little things that make passengers feel relaxed and comfortable.

In our Première de Luxe First Class, we've gone beyond providing attentive service, sleeper seats and gourmet meals with world class wines. We also surround you with all kinds of special touches when you need them. Or undisturbed rest when you don't.

So the next time Paris calls, call your travel agent or **(800) 2-FRANCE.** If you're going to Paris, don't just sit there.

© UTA French Airlines

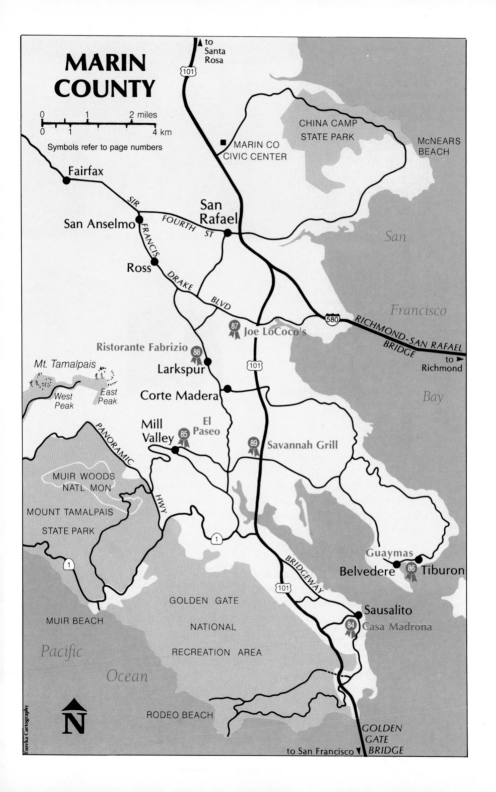

CASA MADRONA

801 BRIDGEWAY
SAUSALITO, CA 94965
(415) 331-5888

Major Credit Cards
Dinner Mon-Sat · Lunch Mon-Fri
Sunday Brunch

Proprietor
John W. Mays

Chef
Kathleen Hoare

Perched high on a hill over-looking the Sausalito harbor, the Casa Madrona Restaurant is a romantic reminder of a less hurried time. A narrow brick path winds by madrones, fragrant pines and an orange tree and leads to what was once a Victorian mansion.

The restaurant retains much of its 1885 charm, but with some welcome modern additions—such as sliding glass walls and a retractable roof over the beautiful outdoor deck. Here, countless men have been driven to propose, intoxicated by the food, the wine and the magnificent view of sea and sky.

Chef Kathleen Hoare allows flavors to speak for themselves in simple, delightful combinations that soothe rather than startle the palate. Add the house-made breads and desserts of Pastry Chef Jill Branch—whose chocolate decadence cake is worth every sinful bite—and you have a recipe for excellence owner John W. Mays has been perfecting for six years.

AVERAGE DINNER FOR TWO: $65

Menu Highlights

SEASONAL MENU

Appetizers

Chilled shellfish with avocado cream ∗
Fried polenta with three sauces ∗ Scallop
& lobster tart ∗ Country game pâté

Entrées

Sonoma rabbit mole with hominy &
platinos ∗ Roasted fresh Texas game hen
stuffed with chévre ∗ Roast rack of lamb
with mint-infused pomegranate sauce

EL PASEO

17 THROCKMORTON AVENUE
NEAR SUNNYSIDE
MILL VALLEY, CA 94941
(415) 388-0741
Major Credit Cards
Open Daily · Dinner Only

Proprietors
Mark Bottmeyer &
Gunter Kollner

Chef
Farnham Hogue

At this most romantic of the *Epicurean Rendezvous* selected restaurants, an old brick pathway leads between two historic stone buildings into a small, cool courtyard of statuary, fountains, greenery and brick archways. Opening the rustic wooden doors into El Paseo is like lifting the lid of a treasure chest. A golden glow from the chandeliers highlights the brick walls and wooden ceiling beams to reproduce the atmosphere of a seventeenth-century European manor.

Here, proprietors Mark Bottmeyer and Gunter Kollner have created a visual and gustatory feast. Equal in ambiance is the contemporary French cuisine of Chef Farnham Hogue, formerly chef at the late, great Café Royale and part of the original Sutter 500 team with Roger Vergé and Hubert Keller.

El Paseo's wine list, with 150,000 bottles in the cellar, won the *Wine Spectator's* Grand Award in 1987 and '88. El Paseo has two private dining rooms, making it a perfect special occasion place. AVERAGE DINNER FOR TWO: $40

Menu Highlights

SEASONAL MENU

Appetizers

Belgian endive, pear, blue cheese & walnut salad, raspberry vinaigrette ∗ Wild mushrooms with puff pastry ∗ Gravlax with Akvavit in dill-mustard sauce

Entrées

Grilled marinated prawns with fennel & mustard ∗ Poached salmon with ginger-lime beurre blanc ∗ Loin of lamb with roasted garlic sauce

MEXICAN

GUAYMAS

5 MAIN STREET
AT THE FERRY LANDING
TIBURON, CA 94920
(415) 435-6300

Major Credit Cards
Open Daily · Lunch & Dinner

General Manager
Hal Finkelstein

Chef
Francisco Cisneros

Like the Mexican fishing village it was named after, Guaymas has the true South-of-the-Border spirit. Its modern adobe setting, bright colors, outdoor patios and waterfront location make it a popular spot to relax and enjoy the view across the bay.

Chef Francisco Cisneros, a native of Jalisco, Mexico, introduces Americans to the true cuisine of Mexico. You won't find the typical combination of burritos and fajitas here, and you won't miss them either. Instead, you'll feast on fresh seasonal fish lightly marinated in lime juice, tamales wrapped in real corn husks or banana leaves, and homemade tortillas and chips that arrive fresh and hot to your table. It's a menu that emphasizes lightness, simplicity and, above all, authenticity.

As you sit back, sip your margarita and look out over the water, it's easy to imagine that you've been transported to the coast of Mexico. AVERAGE DINNER FOR TWO: $35

Menu Highlights

Appetizers

Assorted appetizers: cazuelita, quesadilla, garnachas, chalupa & tostadita ∗ Corn tortilla boats with chicken, jalapeños, red onions, fresh cheese & sour cream

Entrées

Giant shrimp marinated in lime juice & cilantro ∗ Poblano chiles stuffed with chicken & raisins & topped with walnut sauce & pomegranate seeds ∗ Roasted half duck with pumpkin seed sauce

JOE LoCoco's

300 DRAKES LANDING ROAD
AT SIR FRANCIS DRAKE
GREENBRAE, CA 94904
(415) 925-0808

Mastercard & Visa Only
Open Daily for Dinner · Lunch Mon-Fri

Proprietor
Louis J. Rago

Chef/Proprietor
Joe LoCoco

You know you're on to something good when you leave a restaurant to open another and the entire clientele follows *en masse*. Joe LoCoco is the lucky man blessed with such an appreciative following. Due to its unpretentious ambiance and LoCoco's and Louis Rago's considerable talents, the restaurant has been a success since its opening in 1987.

LoCoco, raised in Buffalo, spent time in Livorno, Italy, honing his skills in preparing traditional Italian cuisine. He uses age-old recipes (some dating from medieval times) utilizing fresh vegetables, housemade pasta and wild game to create hearty, peasant-style dishes.

The dining room's peach stucco walls are covered with plates from Siena, paintings from Florence and Tuscan pottery.

Large windows open on views of the bay and Mt. Tamalpais. Dining *al fresco* on the outdoor patio is another way to savor the Tuscan experience. AVERAGE DINNER FOR TWO: $45

Menu Highlights

Appetizers

Grilled duck sausage & radicchio with balsamic vinegar & virgin olive oil ∗ Tuscan bruschetta with fresh tomatoes, olive oil & oregano ∗ Housemade antipasto

Entrées

Snail-shaped pasta with truffles ∗ Ziti with eggplant & ricotta ∗ Grilled veal chop with sage butter ∗ Prawns sautéed with sundried tomatoes, saffron, garlic & herbs

RISTORANTE FABRIZIO

455 MAGNOLIA AVENUE
AT KING
LARKSPUR, CA 94939
(415) 924-3332

Mastercard & Visa Only
Closed Sunday · Dinner Only

Proprietor/Hostess
Marie Martinelli

Chef/Proprietor
Fabrizio Martinelli

An arched entryway decorated with original prints from Lucca, Italy, leads to the Fabrizio dining room. A menu is placed at the table when guests are seated, but attention is best given to the creative daily specials listed on a chalkboard. A lively atmosphere prevails here—tables in close proximity, set with candles, wine bottles, linen and handsome flatware.

Fabrizio Martinelli, born and raised in Lucca, where his parents still live, came to San Francisco at age nineteen. He worked at two of The City's finest restaurants, Amelio's and L'Orangerie, before opening his own. Between his Lucca recipes and fresh seasonal local products, the chef's creative genius has found an outlet for full expression. One house specialty, for example, is linguine with fresh clams and mussels served with garlic, tomatoes and herbs.

Wife Marie Martinelli assists in all facets of the management. The wine list features well-selected Italian bottlings, with helpful descriptions of each. AVERAGE DINNER FOR TWO: $40

Menu Highlights

Appetizers
Cold poached salmon served with cucumber-tarragon sauce * Roasted bell peppers * Eggplant vinaigrette * Baked mozzarella

Entrées
Fetuccine verde with fresh tomato, garlic & basil sauce * Loin of lamb stuffed with spinach, green peppercorn sauce * Quail roasted with pancetta, sage & garlic, served with risotto

AMERICAN

SAVANNAH GRILL

55 TAMAL VISTA
AT MADERA
CORTE MADERA, CA 94925
(415) 924-6774

Major Credit Cards
Open Daily · Lunch & Dinner · Sunday Brunch

Proprietor
Keith Jones

Chef
Jim Romer

In Marin, the Savannah Grill is the place to see and be seen.

With a cherrywood and brass decor created by designer Pat Kuleto, the restaurant is made for people-watching, with a long, narrow dining room overlooking a lively bar on one side and an attractive black-hooded open kitchen on the other.

In this upbeat, unpretentious environment, Chef Jim Romer creates cuisine best described as regional American. Romer concentrates on deftly prepared hardwood grilled and smoked meats and fish, and draws on Asian, Latin and European influences and fresh ingredients to infuse them with intense, distinctive flavors.

Regular patrons definitely have their favorites. "We've tried changing the menu completely, but our customers won't let us," declares Keith Jones. Nevertheless, the bulk of the menu changes every three months, with up to fifteen daily specials spotlighting fresh seafood, salads and pasta dishes. AVERAGE DINNER FOR TWO: $35

Menu Highlights

Appetizers

Grilled eggplant & Bermuda onion with red pepper pesto * Gulf prawns with spicy red curry cream, peanuts & papaya * Beefsteak tomato salad with grilled asparagus

Entrées

Ravioli with provimi veal, Swiss chard, aged cheeses, roasted garlic cream & pesto * Barbecued baby back ribs * Petaluma duck with Roma tomatoes, carrots & roasted garlic

Coffee break. Italian style.

*T*he coffee break in Italy. Rich, meaningful, rewarding. Discover what a coffee break is meant to be with rich, continental style Medaglia d'Oro Espresso. Besides brewing authentic Italian espresso, Medaglia d'Oro is the perfect ingredient for making good things happen, like...

CAFFÈ DANTE

Place one-half an orange slice into a demitasse cup. Pour rich Medaglia d'Oro espresso over orange slice. Add a teaspoon of chocolate syrup and top with whipped cream. Fleck with grated orange rind.

Don't just make coffee.
Make good things happen.

ESPRESSO

Authentic Italian Coffees since 1924.

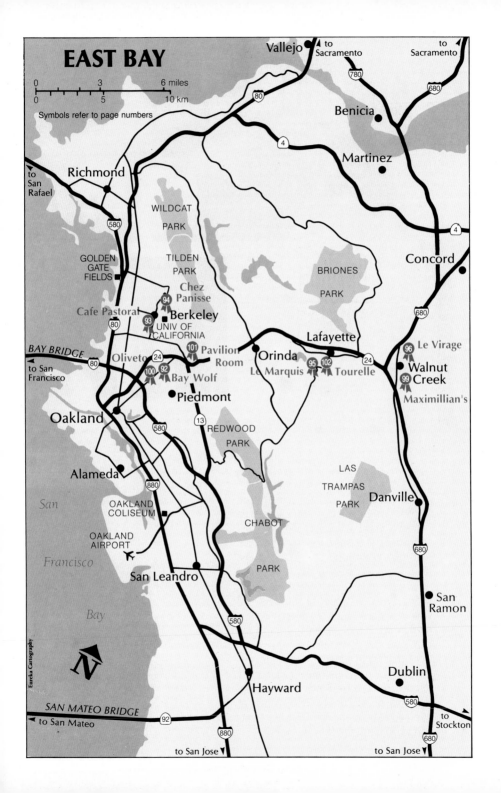

EAST BAY

0 3 6 miles
0 5 10 km

Symbols refer to page numbers

Vallejo

to Sacramento

to Sacramento

Benicia

Martinez

to San Rafael

Richmond

WILDCAT PARK

Concord

GOLDEN GATE FIELDS

TILDEN PARK

BRIONES PARK

Chez Panisse
94

Cafe Pastoral

Berkeley
93

UNIV OF CALIFORNIA

Lafayette

Le Virage
96

BAY BRIDGE

to San Francisco

Oliveto

Pavilion Room
101

Orinda

Le Marquis
95 102 Tourelle

Walnut Creek
99

100 92
Bay Wolf

Maximillian's

Piedmont

13

REDWOOD PARK

Oakland

580

LAS TRAMPAS PARK

Danville

Alameda

San Francisco

880

OAKLAND COLISEUM

CHABOT

PARK

680

OAKLAND AIRPORT

Bay

San Leandro

San Ramon

580

Dublin

N

Eureka Cartography

SAN MATEO BRIDGE

92

Hayward

580

to Stockton

to San Mateo

to San Jose

to San Jose

680

BAY WOLF

3853 PIEDMONT AVENUE
AT RIO VISTA
OAKLAND, CA 94611
(415) 655-6004

Mastercard & Visa Only
Open Daily for Dinner · Lunch Mon-Fri

Proprietor
Larry Goldman
Maitre d'
Mark McLeod

Chef/Proprietor
Michael Wild
Chef
Carol Brendlinger

It is reassuring to know that sincere restaurants are still doing well in this inconstant world. Oakland diners have depended upon Michael Wild and Larry Goldman to keep one step ahead of culinary fads for fourteen years, ever since they took a vacant house and transformed it into the sunny, art-filled oasis that is the Bay Wolf today.

Everything here feels *comme il faut*— the Cinzano umbrellas on the redwood patio, the gleaming brass espresso machine on the bar, and the friendly faces of the experienced waiters and waitresses.

Michael Wild has enjoyed feeding people for as long as he can remember. "I learned homestyle French cooking from my mother," he recalls. "Every meal at our house in Los Angeles was a big event, and when we traveled home to France, it was from one great restaurant to the next." Wild is still in the kitchen every day, designing the monthly menus and daily specials. AVERAGE DINNER FOR TWO: $50

Menu Highlights

MONTHLY MENU

Appetizers

Grilled spiced shrimp with coriander-jalapeño remoulade * Mussel chowder with tasso & andouille sausage

Entrées

Lemon-mint fetuccine with sautéed duck livers * Grilled salmon with tarragon-buttermilk sabayon * Roasted poussin with artichokes, olives & lemon * Roasted leg of lamb with garlic potatoes

CALIFORNIA

CAFE PASTORAL

2160 UNIVERSITY AVENUE
AT OXFORD
BERKELEY, CA 94704
(415) 540-7514
Mastercard & Visa Only
Lunch Tues-Fri · Dinner Tues-Sun

Proprietor
Hi-Suk T. Dong

Chef/Proprietor
Sanju J. Dong

With so many paintings, sculptures and ceramics, Café Pastoral could easily stand on its own as a gallery. And, in fact, it is a gallery, complete with changing exhibits, opening parties, a working studio and even a curator. But the eclectic Café Pastoral is best known for its excellence in the art of fine cuisine.

Korean husband and wife Hi-Suk and Sanju Dong met while students in San Francisco. He is now a practicing architect. She is a painter who creates works of art not only in the studio but also in the kitchen as Café Pastoral's chef.

Drawing from a palette of French, Asian and California influences, Sanju expresses herself in a way that defies categorization. Her technique places equal emphasis on taste and presentation. "Our cuisine is constantly evolving," says Hi-Suk. "Rather than look at each dish separately, I think it's better to judge it as a body of work." And an impressive composition it is. AVERAGE DINNER FOR TWO: $40

Menu Highlights

DAILY MENU

Appetizers

"Axonometric" appetizer of fried wonton skins layered with smoked salmon, tuna sashimi, daikon & sherry-wasabi vinaigrette ∗ Korean-style steak tartare

Entrées

Grilled quail marinated in hot chile bean paste & sesame oil, served with pan-fried noodles ∗ Sautéed salmon with napa cabbage, eggplant & soy-sake sauce

CHEZ PANISSE

1517 SHATTUCK
AT CEDAR
BERKELEY, CA 94701
(415) 548-5525
Major Credit Cards
Closed Sunday & Monday · Dinner Only

☎ ⅲ ♿

Chef/Proprietor
Alice Waters

Chef
Paul Bertolli

Famed for originality, the uncompromising quality of its ingredients and the vision of Alice Waters, Chez Panisse is a great American restaurant with an international reputation.

The free spirit so pervasive in Berkeley also prevails in this kitchen. Since opening in 1971, Chez Panisse has seldom repeated a dish on its prix fixe menu (currently $50). As the culinary shrine of the American food revolution, it has fresh-produce suppliers knocking on the back door every day. Their produce is organically grown and their meat contains no chemicals.

"We're never satisfied," Waters says. "We're always reaching and searching, searching and reaching."

Other culinary heavyweights have cooked here, then gone on to create their own noted kitchens—Jeremiah Tower, Joyce Goldstein and Jean-Pierre Moullé, to name a few. Today, Chef Paul Bertolli shows equal creativity with his own style of seasoning and cooking. AVERAGE DINNER FOR TWO: $100

Menu Highlights

DAILY MENU

Appetizers
Local salmon & green onions in lemon grass broth ∗ Sea scallops aioli with wilted curly endive ∗ Corn & red pepper chowder with corn bread

Entrées
Roast Lewis Ranch lamb with green herb stuffing ∗ Braised Sonoma hen with chanterelles, cabbage & tomatoes ∗ Charcoal-grilled Wolfe Farm quail

FRENCH

LE MARQUIS

3524B MT. DIABLO BLVD.
AT FIRST
LAFAYETTE, CA 94549
(415) 284-4422

Major Credit Cards
Closed Sunday & Monday · Dinner Only

Proprietor
Susan Guerguy

Chef/Proprietor
Robert Guerguy

Le Marquis was one of the first restaurants to serve fine cuisine in Contra Costa County. Since Chef Robert Guerguy opened it in 1978, he has won the loyalty of East Bay gourmets with his classic yet light style.

Located in a Lafayette shopping mall, Le Marquis has recently been remodeled in soft tones of celadon and peach, with a beautiful contemporary bar, lots of mirrors, but the same convenient location and ample parking. An abundance of greenery and fresh flowers in the dining room adds to the pleasant ambiance.

It's a lovely setting for the cuisine of Chef Guerguy, a master saucier with nineteen years of training on the French Riviera, from Nice to Cannes, along with five years at La Bourgogne and Ernie's Restaurant in San Francisco. Equal atten-

tion is given to the presentation and service by a friendly and professional staff under the direction of hostess Susan Guerguy. AVERAGE DINNER FOR TWO: $60

Menu Highlights

Appetizers

Fresh artichoke bottom with red bell pepper mousse * House-smoked salmon, horseradish cream * Snails in mushroom caps with garlic & herbs of Provence

Entrées

Flat salmon sautéed with fresh tarragon & tomato beurre blanc * Sliced breast of duck with raspberry sauce * Medallions of veal sautéed with olives & artichokes

Le Virage

2211 NORTH MAIN STREET
WALNUT CREEK, CA 94596
(415) 933-8484

Major Credit Cards
Closed Monday • Lunch & Dinner

Proprietors
Lolek & Andreina Jasinski

Chefs
Ben Premack &
Jesus Castanada

When you drive through Walnut Creek, you can't miss the brightly painted facade of a little farmhouse tucked in *le virage,* "a bend in the road." Surrounded by stout office buildings, Le Virage stands out like a whimsical monument to a more gracious past.

Undaunted by the shadow of their modern neighbors, owners Lolek and Andreina Jasinski and silent partner Robert Goodwin have been upholding the best traditions of that past for fifteen years. The romantically zany setting has something for everyone: a lively bar, walls of celebrity photos, large dining areas with Toulouse Lautrec-style murals, and many small rooms upstairs.

The traditional food, generously portioned, never disappoints. After the meal, don't be surprised if Lolek Jasinski offers a complimentary rare cognac from his private collection or an old-fashioned ten-layer "pousse-café"—a drink better tried than described. AVERAGE DINNER FOR TWO: $60

Menu Highlights

Appetizers
Caviar Beluga * Smoked salmon garni *
Shrimp bisque with cognac * Caesar salad

Entrées
Veal in cream Champagne sauce * Frog legs
sautéed with garlic * Lobster flamed with
brandy * Steak tartare * Filet mignon
sautéed in butter, shallots & Champagne,
flamed with cognac

THE GRANDEST MARNIER.

Grand Marnier Cent cinquantenaire, an exquisite blend of specially aged cognac with a distinctive hint of wild oranges, was created to commemorate the 150th anniversary of Grand Marnier. Available in a very limited edition. It is the quintessential gift.

How would a Jameson Irish Coffee taste without the coffee?

Wonderful.

Jameson® is smoother than Scotch. It's lighter than Bourbon. No wonder. It's made from the finest barley and the purest water. But even so, the exquisite, distinct taste of Jameson imported premium whiskey is often hidden in coffee.

So next time, enjoy the unique taste of Jameson on the rocks, with a splash or tall with soda. Just tell your bartender, "Give me an Irish Coffee. Hold the coffee. Hold the cream. Hold the sugar. And pour the Jameson." Enjoy.

Give me a Jameson. Hold the coffee.

Maximillian's

1604 LOCUST STREET
NEAR BONANZA
WALNUT CREEK, CA 94596
(415) 932-1474

Major Credit Cards
Closed Sunday • Lunch & Dinner

Proprietor
Max Wolfe

Chef
Bernard Mansard

A dinner at Maximillian's in downtown Walnut Creek can either be California nouvelle or classic French; take your pick. The street-level dining room, decorated in rose and green, has a light, comfortable and upscale feeling. The menu is innovative, featuring California products and an abundance of seafood. A grand-piano player entertains Tuesdays through Saturdays.

The upstairs dining room, oak paneled with old brick touches and dark red carpeting, has a more sedate, traditional ambiance. Here, the cuisine emphasizes classic Continental dishes, and service is more formal.

Proprietor Maximillian Wolfe (Max to his customers) has been in the restaurant industry for twenty-six years. Chef Bernard Mansard prepares fresh seafood and meat dishes that reflect the influences of France, Japan and California. "Cooking is an art," he says. "I feel it, live it and work to perfect my art. It is my life." AVERAGE DINNER FOR TWO: $60

Menu Highlights

Appetizers

Steamed Manila clams * Louisiana oysters on the half shell * Smoked barbecued sturgeon with ginger-butter sauce

Entrées

Gulf shrimp cooked in a sauce of mild curry & bananas * Filet of beef with Roquefort-cognac sauce * Breast of pheasant with chanterelle mushrooms * Rack of lamb

Proprietor
Maggie Klein

Chef
Rick Hackett

OLIVETO

5655 COLLEGE AVENUE
OAKLAND, CA 94618
(415) 547-5356

MasterCard & Visa Only
Dinner Mon-Sat · Lunch Mon-Fri
Breakfast, Lunch, Dinner Daily in Cafe

ITALIAN

Maggie Klein's book, *The Feast of the Olive* (1983), is a celebration of olive oil. The high point of her research, a month-long stay at an eleventh-century Tuscan estate, was the inspiration for her restaurant, Oliveto.

"I wanted my restaurant to evoke a feeling of *la dolce vita,* with an emphasis on grilling, fresh vegetables, salads, stews and good wines," declares Klein. The restaurant and cafe are reminiscent of a villa in Tuscany, with light terracotta plaster walls and Mediterranean warmth.

The informal downstairs cafe is a favorite locals' haunt, offering unusual *tapas* and pizzas. The restaurant upstairs boasts excellent Northern Italian fare, an outstanding wine list featuring French, Italian, Spanish and domestic vintages, and a gifted chef, Rick Hackett. Hackett draws

on his formal classical training and experience in the kitchens of California and Spain to create Oliveto's *cucina rustica.*

AVERAGE DINNER FOR TWO: $50

Menu Highlights

DAILY MENU

Appetizers

Risotto with calamari, shrimp, tomatoes & fresh thyme * Perciatelli pasta with roasted peppers, caramelized onions, marjoram & toasted breadcrumbs

Entrées

Grilled yellowfin tuna with grilled tomato, roasted peppers, tapenade & lemon * Roasted veal breast & pepperoni sausage with white wine, rosemary & tomatoes

CALIFORNIA

PAVILION ROOM

CLAREMONT RESORT HOTEL
ASHBY & DOMINGO AVENUES
OAKLAND, CA 94623
(415) 843-3000

Major Credit Cards
Open Daily • Breakfast, Lunch & Dinner

Food & Beverage Director
William Sander
Managing Director
Jonathan Emerson

Chef
Franklin Biggs

The only resort in the Bay Area, the Claremont Hotel is a California landmark, which was built in 1915 just in time for the Panama-Pacific Exhibition. The venerable hotel commands panoramic views of San Francisco's Bay and bridges from its lofty position in the Oakland Hills.

Over the years, the Claremont has seen many changes. The latest is a full spa and the premiere of spa cuisine at the hotel's Pavilion Room. "Americans have changed their lifestyles," says William Sander. "They're more health-conscious, so we've made healthful changes in our menu."

The inherent challenge, of course, is to prepare food that stands on its own merit, short on sodium and fat, yet long on flavor. Franklin Biggs, formerly of The Lodge at Pebble Beach, meets that challenge admirably. AVERAGE DINNER FOR TWO: $70

Menu Highlights

Appetizers
Broiled scallops on a bed of baby lettuce with julienned vegetables & ginger beurre blanc * Spring lamb pâté with curried mango purée * Chilled seafood platter

Entrées
Braided salmon & sole with red pepper sauce * Free-range chicken breast with sundried tomatoes, basil & olive oil * Roasted tenderloin of beef with mustard, pineapple chutney & Zinfandel sauce

FRENCH

TOURELLE

3565 MT. DIABLO BOULEVARD
AT OAK HILL
LAFAYETTE, CA 94549
(415) 284-3565
Major Credit Cards
Closed Monday · Lunch & Dinner · Sunday Brunch

Proprietor	*Chefs*
Annette Esser	*David Mahler & Ron Ottobre*

Annette Esser's East Bay Restaurant, Tourelle, transports you to the South of France. The experience begins with a walk down a flagstone path past fragrant herb and flower gardens. An ivy-covered 1936 tower and two newer brick wings surround a warm courtyard. There, you'll find handcarved wooden chairs, glass-topped tables and a gently bubbling pond.

One of the most romantic restaurants in the Bay Area, Tourelle has a timeless, very European ambiance. The high vaulted ceilings, brick floors and simple, clean-lined furniture are reminiscent of a medieval chateau. The rustic setting is an elegant showcase for Ron Ottobre and David Mahler's synthesis of classic and nouvelle French cuisine and Tourelle's award-winning wine list.

Across the courtyard from the restaurant is Tourelle Cafe, a lively, casual bistro with an open kitchen. Here you'll find country French fare, unusual salads and simply grilled meats and fish. AVERAGE DINNER FOR TWO: $65

Menu Highlights

MONTHLY MENU

Appetizers
Foie gras & blueberries in filo with blueberry vinegar demi-glace * Smoked tuna carpaccio with lime, cilantro & garlic vinaigrette & daikon-red onion spaghetti

Entrées
Roast saddle of lamb with herbs & green onions in veal & spinach mousseline baked in puff pastry * Roast guinea fowl in endive cream sauce with asparagus mousse

J&B on a date.

J&B Scotch Whisky. Blended and bottled in Scotland by Justerini & Brooks, fine wine and spirit merchants since 1749.
To send a gift of J&B anywhere in the U.S., call 1-800-238-4373. Void where prohibited.

AT LIQUOR BARN
THE CHOICE IS YOURS

At Liquor Barn we pride ourselves on having the largest selection of quality Bordeaux wine: Chateau Gruaud-Larose, 1986 Chateau Beaumont and a variety of other popular vintage Bordeaux.

Hurry on down to your nearest Liquor Barn and discover a world of fine wine at the lowest prices around. You'll find it's a choice decision.

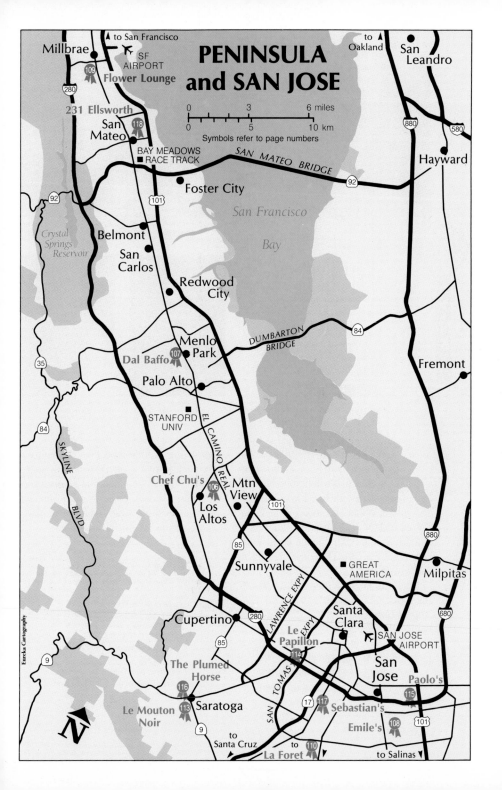

PENINSULA and SAN JOSE

to San Francisco

to Oakland

Millbrae

SF AIRPORT
Flower Lounge
109
280
231 Ellsworth
San Mateo
118

BAY MEADOWS
RACE TRACK

Foster City

San Leandro

880
580
Hayward
SAN MATEO BRIDGE
92

San Francisco Bay

92
Crystal Springs Reservoir
Belmont
San Carlos
101
Redwood City

35
Menlo Park
Dal Baffo 107
Palo Alto
STANFORD UNIV

DUMBARTON BRIDGE
84
Fremont

84
SKYLINE BLVD

EL CAMINO REAL

Chef Chu's
Los Altos 106
Mtn View
101

85
Sunnyvale
GREAT AMERICA

880
Milpitas

Eureka Cartography

9
Cupertino
280
85
The Plumed Horse
116
Le Mouton Noir 113
Saratoga
9
to Santa Cruz

LAWRENCE EXPY
SAN TOMAS EXPY
Le Papillon
114
Santa Clara
SAN JOSE AIRPORT
San Jose
680
115
Paolo's

17 117
Sebastian's
Emile's 108
101
to La Foret 110
to Salinas

Symbols refer to page numbers

0   3   6 miles
0   5   10 km

N

CHEF CHU'S

1067 NORTH SAN ANTONIO ROAD
AT EL CAMINO REAL
LOS ALTOS, CA 94022
(415) 948-2696

Major Credit Cards
Open Daily · Lunch & Dinner

Manager
Norman Chu

Chef/Proprietor
Lawrence Chu

Chef Chu's, in the heart of the Peninsula's El Camino Real nightlife, is a delightful blend of two atmospheres. In the downstairs bar and dining room, the mood is bustling, upbeat and fun. The upstairs dining room is more formal, with a magnificent wood carving of The Nine Dragons covering an entire wall.

Chef Chu is the author of the bestselling cookbook *Chef Chu's Distinctive Cuisine of China,* and is the guiding force behind this restaurant. "To enjoy food," says Chu, "you must be relaxed, in a good mood and in the proper atmosphere."

Chu's spirit is everywhere: he can be seen in the spotless kitchen preparing Lover's Prawns for newlyweds, at a corner table conversing with the United States Secretary of State, or in the lobby,

scrawling a Chinese birthday greeting on the signboard for an 86-year-old guest. Chef Chu is frequently seen on television sharing his wok cooking skills, and is more than happy to advise in menu planning. AVERAGE DINNER FOR TWO: $30

Menu Highlights

A p p e t i z e r s

Catfish roll * Crispy fried shrimp balls * Minced chicken * Potstickers * Smoked fish Shanghai-style

E n t r é e s

Peking duck * Szechuan-style dry braised prawns * Mu shu pork * Prawns with candied pecans in light mustard sauce * Braised whole fresh fish

DAL BAFFO

878 SANTA CRUZ AVENUE
AT UNIVERSITY DRIVE
MENLO PARK, CA 94025
(415) 325-1588

Major Credit Cards
Closed Sunday & Monday · Lunch & Dinner

Proprietor/Manager
Catherine LoGrasso

Chef/Proprietor
Vincenzo LoGrasso

Chef Vincenzo LoGrasso is proud of his elegant restaurant, opened in 1977 near Stanford University in Menlo Park. Trained at the Culinary Academy of Genoa, Italy, LoGrasso is assisted in the kitchen by Chef de Cuisine André Guerguy.

Sicilian pastas are an important part of the menu, but Genoese, French and Californian influences are also represented. The ten to twelve specials offered each day reflect an emphatically fresh and original style.

A spacious bar and lounge area, perfect for a before-dinner wine and an after-dinner espresso, features wood paneling and comfortable lounge chairs. Behind stained-glass doors is a beautifully remodeled banquet room that seats up to forty people. The extraordinary wine list, with exceptional varietals from California, France, Italy, Spain and Germany, has been the recipient of *The Wine Spectator's* Grand Award since 1985. AVERAGE DINNER FOR TWO: $55

Menu Highlights

Appetizers

Mixed mushrooms sautéed with herbs & sourdough toast ∗ Fresh artichokes à la Romana ∗ Petite bouchée of bay scallops with Champagne sauce & spring vegetables

Entrées

Broiled or poached salmon filet with sundried tomatoes & tarragon hollandaise ∗ Medallions of beef with foie gras & black truffle sauce

FRENCH

EMILE'S

545 SOUTH 2ND STREET
NEAR REED
SAN JOSE, CA 95112
(408) 289-1960

Major Credit Cards
Closed Sunday & Monday · Lunch & Dinner

Manager
Christine Mooser

Chef
James Connolly
Chef/Proprietor
Emile Mooser

Chef Emile Mooser, trained in classic old-world style in Lausanne, Switzerland, is mentor to numerous aspiring cooks. Emile's, known affectionately in the South Bay area as a "mother restaurant," is the leader of the restaurant industry here, celebrating its seventeenth year.

Mooser is noted for his detailed attention to seasoning, color and shapes in presentation and to texture of sauces. His managerial skills ensure meticulous service. "My formal training in the wine country above Lake Geneva taught me the intricacies of the proper marriage of food and wine," says Mooser.

Although committed to high standards, he is versatile as well, changing the menu bi-monthly. Chef James Connolly has worked closely with Mooser for nine years to keep the quality consistent. The off-white walls, white linen and upholstered cane chairs provide an intimate, plush setting that highlights the cuisine. AVERAGE DINNER FOR TWO: $65

Menu Highlights

BI-MONTHLY MENU

Appetizers

House-cured salmon with a yogurt-dill sauce ✶ Housemade pork & chicken sausage with braised leeks in vinaigrette ✶ Burgundy snails baked in garlic-lemon butter

Entrées

Grilled marinated seasonal fish with ginger & Japanese mushrooms ✶ Lightly breaded chicken breast sautéed with a lemon-butter sauce

CHINESE

FLOWER LOUNGE

1671 EL CAMINO REAL
AT PARK PLACE
MILLBRAE, CA 94030
(415) 878-8108

Major Credit Cards
Open Daily · Lunch & Dinner

Proprietor
Alice Wong

Chef
Philip Lo

When Alice Wong first came to the Bay Area to study economics at Mills College, she expected to join her family's garment business after graduation. Upon her return to Hong Kong, however, she found her family had started a successful chain of celebrated restaurants called Flower Lounge. That was all it took to change her plans.

An ambitious woman, Wong set out to change the American conception of Cantonese food as bland, with little to offer besides unexciting egg rolls and chop suey. She returned to the Bay Area to open the first Flower Lounge outside Hong Kong.

Wong brought Chef Philip Lo back with her to create the subtly spiced, seafood-dominant dishes that are the trademarks of authentic Cantonese haute cuisine.

"We spend more time on preparation and less on actual cooking, so that the natural flavors of the ingredients are retained, not masked," says Wong. AVERAGE DINNER FOR TWO: $30

Menu Highlights

Appetizers

Shredded duck with fresh fruits * Chicken salad rainbow * Fried seafood with crispy nest * Squab braised in beer * Barbecued spareribs

Entrées

Fried prawns with glazed walnuts in special sauce * Baked crab Hunan-style * Braised tofu with minced shrimp * Shredded beef in black pepper sauce with green onions on iron platter * Squabs with mango

LA FORÊT

21747 BERTRAM ROAD
AT NEW ALMADEN
SAN JOSE, CA 95120
(408) 997-3458

Major Credit Cards
Dinner Tues-Sun • Sunday Brunch

FRENCH

Proprietor	Chef
John Davoudi	Ken Davoudi

The name "San Jose" usually conjures up visions of the Silicon Valley's commerce, computers and crowded freeways. Just a short drive away, untouched by the high-tech hustle and bustle, is the historic village of New Almaden. Its prime attraction, La Forêt, is a quaint brookside restaurant housed in what was the first two-story adobe hotel in California.

A romantic, elegant restaurant warmed by soft candlelight, La Forêt captures the feeling of a French country inn, with original 1848 paneling and ceilings, and big sash windows hung with floral curtains. Tuxedoed waiters offer cordial, old-fashioned service. In this tranquil setting, you can't help but feel soothed and pampered.

John Davoudi has filled his wine list with the best California and France have to offer. His brother Ken creates contemporary versions of traditional French cuisine. Ken's specialty is game, deftly prepared so as to bring out its robust flavors.

AVERAGE DINNER FOR TWO: $70

Menu Highlights

Appetizers
Prawns Bordelaise sautéed in butter, garlic & wine sauce ∗ Escargots in garlic butter ∗ La Forêt salad of Bay shrimp, mushrooms, spinach, pimento & Belgian endive with vinaigrette

Entrées
Veal Normand with butter, shallots, shiitake mushrooms, light cream, wine & Calvados ∗ Tournedos of beef with shallots, truffle essence, Madeira & pâté de foie gras

"She was Law Review.
And she drinks Johnnie Walker"

Good taste is always an asset.

© 1988 Schieffelin & Somerset Co., New York, NY, Blended Scotch Whisky 43.4% Alc/Vol (86.8°).

The AM side of the most complete
guide to Northern California lists the
best of the Bay Area's daytime
activities, including sights,
shopping, museums, art
galleries, antiques, outdoor
dining and beauty salons,
with a full-size map
of Northern California
to guide you.
Flip it over and ...

YOU'RE GOING TO FLIP FOR AM/PM

The PM side tells you everything you
need to know about San Francisco's
nightlife, from restaurants,
theatres, bars and clubs to where
to get a meal after midnight, and
takes you out of town to
Carmel, Monterey,
Sonoma and Napa.

Proprietor
Don Durante

Chef
Jeff Huff

Le Mouton Noir

14560 Big Basin Way
NEAR HIGHWAY 9
Saratoga, CA 95070
(408) 867-7017

Major Credit Cards
Open Daily for Dinner · Lunch Tues-Sat

FRENCH

LE PAPILLON

410 SARATOGA AVENUE
AT KIELY
SAN JOSE, CA 95129
(408) 296-3730

Major Credit Cards
Closed Sunday · Lunch & Dinner

Proprietor
Mike Mashayekh

Chef
Daniel Alezeau

When Mike Mashayekh opened Le Papillon in 1977, he knew that for an executive, the choice of restaurant can be the key to closing a successful business deal.

His fashionable San Jose establishment is now a favorite spot for local business people, who entertain clients there in a toney atmosphere that appeals to pleasure-seekers as well. The soft lighting, pastel walls, glass room dividers, original French prints, mounted butterflies, flowers and greenery all reflect a thoughtful designer's touch.

When the artistry of Chef Daniel Alezeau goes to work on the taste buds, business becomes the last thing on one's mind. Alezeau's creativity is most apparent in the light and fresh sauces he prepares daily to enhance his fresh fish, poultry and meat dishes. Savor this list: thyme-horseradish, pomegranate, raspberry beurre blanc, thistle-honey orange. Le Papillon means butterfly—an appropriate image for the brilliance of this chef's creations. AVERAGE DINNER FOR TWO: $60

Menu Highlights

Appetizers

Linguine fruit de mer ∗ Crab & grapefruit mold ∗ Fetuccine with wild mushroom sauce ∗ Scallops with saffron-dill sauce ∗ Herbed pâté

Entrées

Breast of pheasant in honey-orange sauce ∗ Filet of wild boar in thyme-horseradish sauce ∗ Veal & lobster in mustard-caper sauce ∗ Breast of partridge in red currant sauce

PAOLO'S

520 EAST SANTA CLARA
AT 12TH
SAN JOSE, CA 95112
(408) 294-2558

Major Credit Cards
Closed Sunday • Lunch & Dinner

Manager
Jalil Samavarchian
Proprietor
Jenny Griesbach

Chef/Proprietor
Carolyn Allen
Chef
Clyde Griesbach

"The eyes of the owner fatten the horse" was a favorite saying of the attentive and sharp-eyed Jack Allen, who guided Paolo's through forty illustrious thing new, something that is the direct voice of the second generation." With an international rep

Proprietors
Yvonne & Klaus Pache

Chef
Kevin Gilday

THE PLUMED HORSE

14555 BIG BASIN WAY
HIGHWAY 9
SARATOGA, CA 95070
(408) 867-4711

Major Credit Cards
Closed Sunday · Dinner Only

The picturesque yet sophisticated town of Saratoga is in a historic lumber-and-wine-producing area on the edge of the verdant Santa Cruz Mountains. The Plumed Horse, a mix of Victorian and American styles, sets its own vintage tone.

Proprietors Klaus and Yvonne Pache give each diner all the care and attention they would lavish on any guest in their home. Chef Kevin Gilday, a graduate of the Culinary Institute of America in Hyde Park, New York, shares the Paches' dedication. "I have a commitment to the traditional values of The Plumed Horse's thirty-five-year history in the Santa Clara Valley," he says "We have a loyal clientele who are happy with our classic cuisine. But I try to be innovative with my specials, such as poached oysters baked in a pastry shell."

The colorful and lively Crazy Horse Lounge offers grand-piano entertainment and live music for dancing on the weekends. An exceptional wine list earned The Plumed Horse *The Wine Spectator's* Grand Award. AVERAGE DINNER FOR TWO: $75

Menu Highlights

SEASONAL MENU

Appetizers

Cabernet-braised mushroom caps with sea scallops * Dry-aged carpaccio with peanut-mustard sauce * Lobster in spinach bundles with truffle sauce

Entrées

Roasted Santa Cruz mountain quail with plum wine sauce * Saddle of venison with braised pears & wild mushrooms * Young Sonoma rack of lamb

AWARD WINNER

Sebastian's

1901 S. Bascom Avenue
AT HAMILTON
Campbell, CA 95008
(408) 377-8600

Major Credit Cards
Open Daily for Dinner · Lunch Mon-Fri

Manager
Gavin Gracey

Chef
Michael Hart

From its perch on the seventeenth floor of the Pruneyard Towers, the tallest building

Sebastian's.

The elegant restaurant's romantic lighting and views of twinkling city lights make

231 ELLSWORTH

231 SOUTH ELLSWORTH STREET
AT THIRD AVENUE
SAN MATEO, CA 94401
(415) 347-7231

Major Credit Cards
Dinner Mon-Sat · Lunch Mon-Fri

Proprietor
Ken Ottoboni

Chef/Proprietor
Kurt Grasing

In 1988, the two-year-old 231 Ellsworth emerged out of nowhere to win the *San Francisco Focus* People's Choice Award for the Peninsula's best French restaurant. Behind this "instant" success, however, were thirteen years of planning, begun when Ken Ottoboni and Kurt Grasing met at San Francisco's Clift Hotel.

The first spent the years working toward his "lifetime dream" at such restaurants as Le Castel and Fleur de Lys, while the second honed his skills at Narsai's, New York's Pierre Hotel and London's only three-star restaurant, Le Gavroche. Together, they have earned a well-deserved place in the spotlight with fresh, modern versions of French cuisine and a well-chosen collection of 200 French and California wines in every price range.

231 Ellsworth features a seasonal à la carte menu, a four-course, prix-fixe menu and sensational desserts by Pastry Chef Phil Ogiela. No wonder it's the people's choice. AVERAGE DINNER FOR TWO: $60

Menu Highlights

SEASONAL MENU

Appetizers

Smoked salmon with terrine of avocado ∗ Sautéed scallops with passionfruit & grains of caviar ∗ Summer salad with green beans, duck aspic & duck confit

Entrées

Medallions of venison with corn & white beans ∗ Seared ahi with roasted eggplant & basil ∗ Breast of duck with raspberries & bittersweet chocolate

THE WINE WORLD LEADERS PREFER.

President Reagan and Soviet leader Gorbachev drink a toast with La Crema wine at the 1988 World Summit in Moscow.

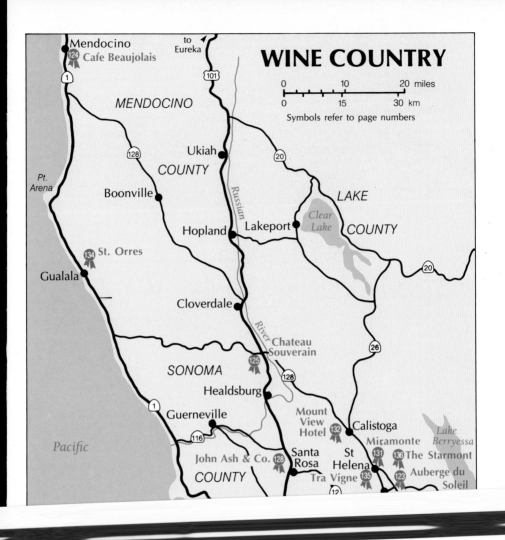

WINE COUNTRY

0   10   20 miles
0   15   30 km

Symbols refer to page numbers

Mendocino
124 Cafe Beaujolais
1

to Eureka
101

MENDOCINO

128
Ukiah
COUNTY

Pt. Arena

Boonville

Russian

LAKE

Hopland   Lakeport   Clear Lake   COUNTY

20

20

134 St. Orres

Gualala

Cloverdale

River   Chateau Souverain

26

SONOMA

125

128

Healdsburg

1

Guerneville

Mount View Hotel   132 Calistoga

Lake Berryessa

116

Miramonte

Pacific

John Ash & Co. 128   Santa Rosa

COUNTY

St Helena

131   136 The Starmont

Tra Vigne   135   123   Auberge du Soleil

12

"So Luxurious
It Makes You Feel Wicked."

- LOS ANGELES TIMES

L'ERMITAGE HOTELS

A Collection of Originals

Beverly Hills • West Hollywood
800/424-4443

AUBERGE DU SOLEIL

**180 RUTHERFORD HILL ROAD
RUTHERFORD, CA 94573
(707) 963-1211**

*Mastercard & Visa Only
Open Daily · Lunch & Dinner*

Maître d'
Stephen Goldberg

Chef
Albert Tordjman

Napa Valley, world famous for great wines, is the setting for Auberge du Soleil, equally noted for hospitality and cuisine. Casual by day, tomatoes instead of butter and cream."

The lunch menu is an à la carte selection, while the dinner menu is prix fixe (*47*).

CAFE BEAUJOLAIS

961 UKIAH STREET
NEAR EVERGREEN
MENDOCINO, CALIFORNIA 95460
(707) 937-5614

No Credit Cards Accepted
Dinner Thurs-Sun • Breakfast & Lunch Daily

Chef/Proprietor
Margaret Fox

Chef
Christopher Kump

Mendocino has long been known as an innovative artists' colony and as a picturesque, cool coastal retreat. Now it is also known as a haven for gourmets, thanks to Margaret Fox and her Cafe Beaujolais.

Located on a side street in a 1910 Victorian, Cafe Beaujolais was first heralded for its astonishing breakfasts, brunches and lunches. "I love breakfast," Fox says. "It's the forgotten meal, and yet people are so appreciative when they have one that is outstanding."

Recently, Fox and Chef Kump have been placing equal emphasis on the à la carte dinners available Thursday through Sunday from April to December. Specialties of the house feature local produce and seafood prepared with an eclectic American and French style.

Chef Fox markets her Panforte de Mendocino and Beaujolais Fruitcake; now visitors can take a little bit of Mendocino home. The list of California wines changes frequently to include new releases and select vintages. AVERAGE DINNER FOR TWO: $60

Menu Highlights

SEASONAL MENU

Appetizers

Fresh leek terrine with house-cured bacon & shiitake mushroom vinaigrette *
Thai smoked-beef salad with chiles, mint & cilantro

Entrées

Roast filet of beef with Roquefort sauce & toasted almonds, walnuts & pinenuts *
Local salmon braised in butter & white wine, with basil & bok choy

CHATEAU SOUVERAIN

400 SOUVERAIN ROAD
AT INDEPENDENCE LANE/HWY 101
GEYSERVILLE, CA 95441
(707) 433-3141

Major Credit Cards
Dinner Thurs-Sat · Lunch Tues-Sat

Assistant Managers
Susan Mauldin &
Richard Duran

Chef & Executive Chef
Richard Bruno
& Gary Danko

The view from The Restaurant at Chateau Souverain has always been one of the most spectacular in the wine country. Set atop a

with a wealth of fresh fruit, vegetables, cheeses and meats," says Danko. "But it is what you do with these ingredients that sets you apart."

DOMAINE CHANDON

CALIFORNIA DRIVE
AT HIGHWAY 29
YOUNTVILLE, CA 94599
(707) 944-2892

Major Credit Cards
Closed Monday & Tuesday • Lunch & Dinner

Manager
Daniel Shanks

Chef
Philippe Jeanty

When the great houses of Champagne, Moet and Chandon, came to the United States and established Domaine Chandon in the high-profile Napa Valley, oenophiles expected a great American sparkling wine, and they have not been disappointed. They got even more than they bargained for: a fine French restaurant.

Chef Philippe Jeanty of Epernay, France, trained at the Reims Culinary Academy in the heart of Champagne, was appointed chef de cuisine at Domaine Chandon in 1978. "I style my cuisine to reflect California's openness to innovation, the readily available fresh products and the great traditions of French cooking," he says. "And," he adds with a sparkle in his eyes, "I emphasize foods compatible with Champagne."

Manager and Maitre d' Daniel Shanks maintains Moet et Chandon's 400-year tradition of hospitality, presenting the cuisine with professional flair but without unnecessary flourish. AVERAGE DINNER FOR TWO: $80

Menu Highlights

SEASONAL MENU

Appetizers

Home-smoked salmon salad with shallots & balsamic vinegar ∗ Artichoke hearts pickled in Chandon Brut with asiago cheese

Entrées

Loin of rabbit with Champagne-rosemary sauce ∗ Sweetbreads with shallot butter, truffle juice & Cabernet essence ∗ Roasted salmon with chervil butter, paper-thin potato chips

The Grille

SONOMA MISSION INN & SPA
18140 SONOMA HIGHWAY 12
BOYES HOT SPRINGS, CA 95416
(707) 938-9000

Major Credit Cards
Open Daily ★ Lunch & Dinner ★ Sunday Brunch

Hotel Manager
Peter Henry

Chef
Charles Saunders

Forty miles north of San Francisco is Northern California's largest, most luxurious spa, the Sonoma Mission Inn & Spa. Built in 1927 on a site reverical and simple matter to prepare great food." His cuisine favors direct, strong flavors with an emphasis on local seafood and vegetables

Managers
*Karen Armstrong,
Elizabeth J. Dudley &
Gregory Zoeller*

Chef/Proprietor
John Ash

JOHN ASH & CO.

4330 BARNES ROAD
NEAR HIGHWAY 101 & RIVER RD.
SANTA ROSA, CA 95401
(707) 527-7687

Major Credit Cards
Open Daily · Lunch & Dinner

Since he opened his restaurant in 1980, John Ash has been dubbed "one of the twenty-five hot new chefs in America" by *Food and Wine* magazine. This accolade echoes the sentiments of diners who have savored Ash's cooking. Ash responds to the lavish praise with modesty: "I'm just a refugee from the corporate world."

His cuisine, however, says otherwise. Consistently artistic and inspired, it features the freshest bounty from Sonoma's boutique farms and innovatively revised recipes from all over the world. "America is a mix of all peoples; my food is the same," he says. "California cuisine means using flavors and techniques from various ethnic recipes to create food that is fun, different and alive with flavor." To achieve this, Ash calls on his training, which includes a degree in art along with culinary schooling in Europe and the United States.

Located next to the Vintners Inn, his restaurant combines Sonoma charm, vineyard views and terrace dining. AVERAGE DINNER FOR TWO: $60

Menu Highlights

Appetizers

Rillette of duck with green peppercorns & fresh chutney * Hog Island oysters warmed with crab

Entrées

Boned quail stuffed with pancetta, walnuts & leeks * Grilled pork tenderloin with fresh shiitake mushrooms * Aged New York steak with a Jack Daniels sauce

Proprietor
Edouard Platel

Chef/Proprietor
Udo Nechutnys

MIRAMONTE

1327 RAILROAD AVENUE
NEAR HUNT
ST. HELENA, CA 94574
(707) 963-3970

Credit Cards Not Accepted
Closed Monday & Tuesday · Dinner Only

Within a restored French Provencal-style hotel dating back to 1907 in picturesque St. Helena, affable host Edouard Platel showcases the culinary talents of Chef Udo Nechutnys. Blending his classical French technique with an Oriental discipline and feeling for the origins and purposes of food, Nechutnys offers an intriguing and imaginative menu.

Ever faithful to the time-honored principles of great cuisine, his recipes also reflect the current concern for health and fitness. Udo credits the great red wines of Napa Valley, which he uses regularly in his cooking, for the subtle flavors in his menu.

In addition to the two elegant dining rooms, a cool patio and a quiet back room tavern are available for warm weather

dining. As Platel and Nechutnys believe in the old-world style of dining, allow for an extended evening to savor the unique blend of cuisine and ambiance that is Miramonte. AVERAGE DINNER FOR TWO: $90

Menu Highlights

Appetizers

Smoked salmon ✳ Marinated eggplant with sundried tomatoes ✳ Foie gras de Paul Bocuse ✳ Quenelles St. Jacques Orléanaise

Entrées

Lamb with yogurt sauce ✳ Roast breast of duck with prunes ✳ Pigeon à la Provencal, with herbs & cognac sauce ✳ Salmon on a bed of spinach

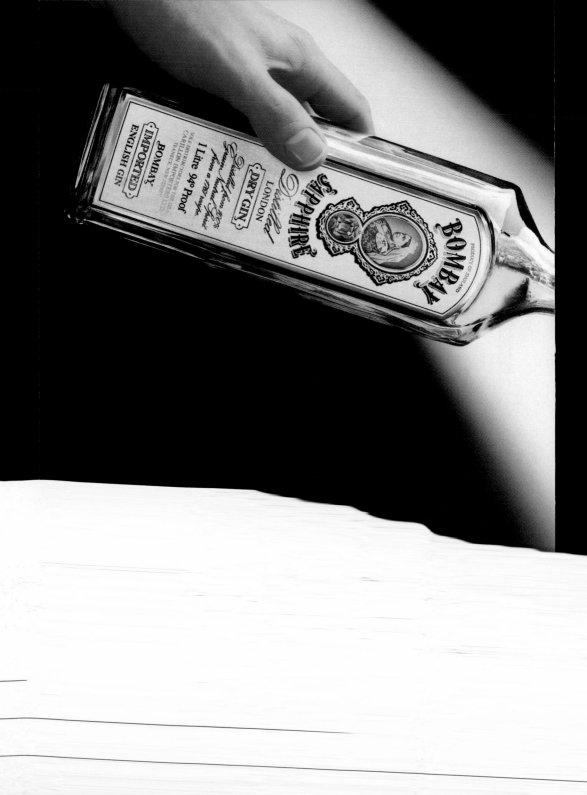

The gin is unprecedented in its creation. The bottle is unprecedented in its beauty. Bombay Sapphire.

Distilled with rare and precious botanicals including Coriander Seeds from Morocco, Grains of Paradise from the

Gold Coast and Cubeb Berries from Java. A total of ten of the most unusual flavors on Earth.

Their spirit is preserved in Sapphire's unique distillation where the gin vapors pass through each botanical, one by one.

Bombay Sapphire. As complex and extraordinary as the jewel that was its namesake.

MOUNT VIEW HOTEL

1457 LINCOLN BOULEVARD
AT WASHINGTON AVENUE
CALISTOGA, CA 94515
(707) 942-6877

Major Credit Cards
*Open Daily * Breakfast, Lunch & Dinner*

General Manager
Scott Ullrich
Food & Beverage Director
Michel Millet

Chef
Paul Rankin

The Mount View Hotel has an Art Deco flavor that extends to the comfortable, light-filled dining room. Yet the cuisine is thoroughly modern, a spectacular combination of classic French techniques with American and Asian influences.

The man responsible for turning out some of the most exciting food in the Napa Valley is Chef Paul Rankin. Working with the renowned Roux brothers in London's Le Gavroche, Rankin became a master of what he calls "New Classic French Cuisine." How does sliced breast of duck on mushroom pasta with apples and black currants sound? Or a steamed symphony of seafood in a ginger and Thai basil cream sauce?

Affable General Manager Scott Ullrich shares the responsibility for the restaurant's success. Under his direction, the restaurant was rated "15" by Gault Millau as one of Northern California's top ten restaurants, and the wine list has been awarded the *Wine Spectator's* Top 100 Award. AVERAGE DINNER FOR TWO: $60

Menu Highlights

SEASONAL MENU

Appetizers

Composed plate of smoked salmon with sliced radish, sesame & ginger * Fresh foie gras sautéed crisp with a warm potato salad & hazelnut vinaigrette

Entrées

Roast leg of Roe buck venison with wild rice, leeks & juniper butter sauce * Crusty filet of wild California salmon on watercress pasta with Champagne beurre blanc

CALIFORNIA

MUSTARDS GRILL

**7399 ST. HELENA HIGHWAY 29
YOUNTVILLE, CA 94599
(707) 944-2424**

*Mastercard & Visa Only
Open Daily · Lunch & Dinner*

*Proprietors
Bill Higgins & Bill Upson*

*Chef/Proprietor
Cindy Pawlcyn*

Partners Bill Higgins, Bill Upson and Cindy Pawlcyn, realizing the restaurant kitchen is the new theater in American life, placed an open cooking area with an oak, madrone and manzanita wood-burning grill and birch-burning oven in the middle of their lively Napa Valley restaurant.

Center stage here is Chef Pawlcyn, who follows a self-directed path: graduate of the University of Wisconsin Restaurant School, trained at the Pump Room in Chicago, chef at the posh Meadowood Country Club, menu creator and equal partner in the three successful Real Restaurants. She has received rave reviews. Her dishes are stylish and light, characterized by unusual herbs, fish grilled over various types of wood, oven-smoked meats and the North Coast's unusual boutique vegetables.

The ambiance at Mustards is lively and youthful. Local winemakers often gather at the wine bar to sip one of the many varietals available by the glass. AVERAGE DINNER FOR TWO: $40

Menu Highlights

SEASONAL MENU

Appetizers

Warm goat cheese with walnuts & bitter greens ✳ Seared rare tenderloin served chilled with Japanese marinade ✳ Mixed greens with blue cheese & seasoned pecans

Entrées

Mongolian pork chop with hot sweet mustard ✳ Smoked duck with warm tomato mango salsa ✳ Pounded chicken breast with tomatillo salsa

St. Orres

36601 Hwy. 1 South
NORTH OF TOWN
GUALALA, CA 95445
(707) 884-3335

Credit Cards Not Accepted
Seasonal Schedule · Dinner Only

Proprietor
Charles Black

Chef/Proprietor
Rosemary Campiformio

CALIFORNIA

St. Orres dates back to 1820, when the George St. Orres family settled the area now known as Gualala. Today, the reconstructed St. Orres inn and restaurant, designed by Eric Black, overlooks the magnificent Mendocino coast.

Inspired by Russian architecture, the dining room and lodge are dominated by two onion-shaped domes and were built with one-hundred-year-old timber. Inside, a country-inn atmosphere prevails: an all-natural-wood bar area with a beautiful rock fireplace greets guests at the entrance, and the wall hangings, woven rugs, pictures and lounge furniture are all the work of local artisans.

Every day, under the direction of Rosemary Campiformio, the kitchen prepares food that reflects a California "North Coast" cuisine. Wild boar, venison, wild mushrooms, sea urchin, mussels, salmon and lamb predominate; the produce is locally grown; and the herbs are fresh from the St. Orres garden. AVERAGE DINNER FOR TWO: $55

Menu Highlights

DAILY MENU

Appetizers

Sea urchin mousse ✳ Venison pâté with huckleberries & pistachios ✳ House-cured gravlax ✳ Fresh basil ravioli with sundried tomatoes, wild mushrooms & cream

Entrées

Salmon with nasturtiums & saffron ✳ Wild boar with Zinfandel & blackberries ✳ Stuffed loin of lamb with fresh rosemary

ITALIAN

TRA VIGNE

1050 CHARTER OAK
AT ST. HELENA HWY.
ST. HELENA, CA 94574
(707) 963-4444

Mastercard & Visa Only
Open Daily · Lunch & Dinner

Proprietor
Kevin Cronin

Chef/Proprietor
Michael Chiarello

The wildly successful people at Real Restaurants have put their Midas touch on yet another popular eatery. Located in a landmark stone building (formerly St. George Restaurant), Tra Vigne is Napa Valley's newest favorite, attracting an animated crowd day and night.

The cuisine is what Michael Chiarello likes to call "American food prepared with the heart, hands and eyes of an Italian." Everything is made on the premises — prosciutto, cheeses, breads, pastas, gelati — from ultra-fresh local ingredients.

The decor packs a striking visual punch. Limn Co.'s talented Michael Guthrie has created a neo-gothic feel, with gilt and high-tech accents softened by old-world touches like ash tables and rush-seated chairs. The vine-covered brick courtyard provides a tranquil alternative to the action inside. AVERAGE DINNER FOR TWO: $50

Menu Highlights

Appetizers

Grilled mozzarella and prosciutto in romaine, tomato vinaigrette * Grilled radicchio with black olive & Zinfandel sauce * Smoked prosciutto with figs, virgin olive oil & black pepper

Entrées

Fetuccine with grilled artichoke, sweet corn & chervil * Double-cut lamb chops with basil, fennel & black pepper * Grilled rabbit with mustard, sage & juniper

THE STARMONT

MEADOWOOD RESORT
900 MEADOWOOD LANE
ST. HELENA, CA 94574
(707) 963-3646

Major Credit Cards
Daily for Dinner · Breakfast & Lunch in The Grill

FRENCH

Managing Director
Maurice Nayrolles

Chef
Hervé Glin

Nestled in its own small valley at the end of a country lane, Meadowood is just off the Silverado Trail, minutes outside St. Helena. Yet this beautiful resort is so secluded and luxurious that visitors immediately feel miles away from the rest of the world. Located on the upper level of the clubhouse, The Starmont's formal interior and large decks look out onto the immaculate golf course, croquet lawns and the wooded hills beyond.

Chef Hervé Glin, trained in the restaurants of his native Brittany and in Paris, came to Meadowood one year ago from Washington, D.C., at the very time he was named one of the top six chefs there. His cuisine brings out the flavors of Northern California's abundant fresh products.

Meadowood's extensive wine list, in-cluding over ninety Cabernets, offers wines from the established Napa Valley wineries as well as selections from the newcomers. AVERAGE DINNER FOR TWO: $80

Menu Highlights

SEASONAL MENU

Appetizers

Open-faced ravioli of sea scallops & coriander on vine-ripened tomato marinara

Entrées

Maine lobster sauté with tomato angelhair on watercress with pesto sauce ∗ Sautéed Petaluma rabbit loin with confit pearl onions & rosemary cream ∗ Baked lamb loin with Petaluma escargots & garlic custard

Meadowood
Napa Valley

A World Apart in the Napa Valley

Fireplace Suites, Fairway Grill,
The Starmont Restaurant,
Tennis, Golf, Croquet, Pool,
Massage, Hiking Trails,
Wine School

Meadowood Resort • 900 Meadowood Lane • St. Helena, CA 94574
TEL (707) 963-3646 FAX (707) 963-3532

*L*aced throughout the Inn's wooded acres are flowering walkways, three hidden hot tubs ...and scores of cottage-like Sur Rooms, Suites and Townhouses. Consider one of the Suites or Townhouse units, it offers a custom-furnished parlor, full kitchen, master bedroom, and bath with massive spa tub. Each accommodation includes a wood-burning fireplace and vista deck. Valet parking, concierge service, room service and a host of pampering room amenities are provided.

The Highlands Inn. At the edge of Big Sur, and minutes from the incomparable shops, galleries and seaside attractions of Carmel & Monterey. Visit soon.

HIGHLANDS INN

Just South of Carmel on Highway 1
P.O. Box 1700
Carmel, California 93921
(408)624-3801

For Reservations Call
Your Travel Agent
Or Toll Free (800)583-9525
From California (800)682-4811

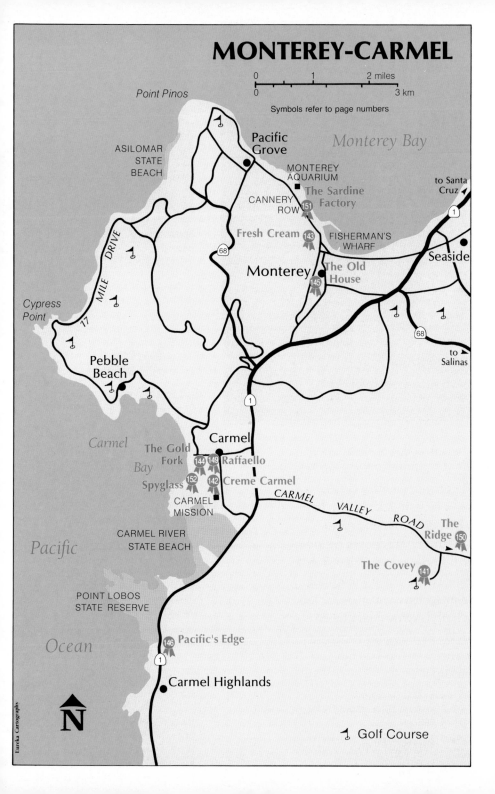

MONTEREY-CARMEL

Symbols refer to page numbers

Point Pinos

ASILOMAR STATE BEACH

Pacific Grove

Monterey Bay

to Santa Cruz

MONTEREY AQUARIUM

CANNERY ROW

The Sardine Factory 151

Fresh Cream 143

FISHERMAN'S WHARF

Seaside

Cypress Point

MILE DRIVE

17

68

Monterey

The Old House 145

68

to Salinas

Pebble Beach

Carmel Bay

Pacific

The Gold Fork 144 149 **Raffaello**

Spyglass 152 142 **Creme Carmel**

CARMEL MISSION

CARMEL RIVER STATE BEACH

Carmel

CARMEL VALLEY ROAD

The Ridge 150

The Covey 141

POINT LOBOS STATE RESERVE

Ocean

146 **Pacific's Edge**

1

Carmel Highlands

N

Golf Course

Eureka Cartography

QUAIL
LODGE

AT THE CARMEL VALLEY
GOLF & COUNTRY CLUB

Quail Lodge is situated on the grounds of a beautiful private country club which, in addition to its 18-hole golf course, provides a wide variety of services for our Quail Lodge guests. The Club dining room offers a tempting and imaginative menu selection for both breakfast and lunch. Our cocktail lounge is perfect for afternoon and evening relaxation.

Please contact Miss Carla Taylor
8205 Valley Greens Drive   Carmel, California 93923
(408) 624-1581

Luxurious guest rooms that change your every expectation into delightful reality

Mobil ★★★ Travel Guide   MEMBER
PREFERRED **H**OTELS WORLDWIDE

The only Mobil 5-star resort between San Francisco and Los Angeles.

EUROPEAN

The Covey

QUAIL LODGE
8205 VALLEY GREENS DRIVE
CARMEL, CA 93923
(408) 624-1581

Major Credit Cards
Open Daily · Dinner Only

General Manager
Csaba Ajan

Executive Chef
Bob Williamson

Exquisite cuisine with a California flair in a spa and country club atmosphere—it's all yours at Quail Lodge in Carmel, where the undulating Carmel River meanders around a golf course and ten picturesque lakes.

The Covey restaurant's natural wood interiors give it a warm, homey feeling, while its large glass windows and skylights bring in the beauty of the outdoors.

The Covey presents an à la carte menu that reflects Chef Bob Williamson's classical training in Switzerland. His European touch is leavened with a distinctively American style, the result of years spent in Oregon, Chicago and Canada and the availability of California's abundant year-round garden harvests.

Here, sauces are light, the vegetables are *al dente* and the garnishes feature the artichokes and avocados of the Monterey Peninsula. The wine list features a superb selection of hard to find California wines.

AVERAGE DINNER FOR TWO: $70

Menu Highlights

Appetizers

Beluga caviar * Quenelles * Swedish-style rainbow trout * Clam & mussel cream soup * Escargots Gilroy

Entrées

Fresh Morro Bay abalone * Scallop of Scandinavian elk with Port & shallots * Scampi sautéed in olive oil with garlic, sage, lemon, clam juice & Pernod * Fresh fish of the day

CRÈME CARMEL

SAN CARLOS
BETWEEN OCEAN & SEVENTH AVENUES
CARMEL, CA 93921
(408) 624-0444

Mastercard & Visa Only
Open Daily • Dinner Only

Proprietor
Cynthia Ling

Chef/Proprietor
Craig Ling

Simplicity and clarity are Chef/ Proprietor Craig Ling's main concerns at Crème Carmel. Clean, straight lines, spare graphics and white linens make up the understated decor. The light, fresh cuisine follows a similar theme.

"Quality is first," says Ling. "We're aware of culinary fashions, but we're suspicious of the avant-garde. Our ideal is to be creative with an underlying direct-ness."

The French character of the menu gains distinction from a subtle lightening of sauces. They do not overwhelm the food, they accent it.

Because Chef Ling likes to take advantage of seasonal products, Crème Carmel's menu offers a printed list of daily specials that is just as lengthy as the regular menu. That extends to the desserts since the wine list includes a singular collection of Sauternes, Barsacs and California late harvest dessert wines, too often overlooked elsewhere. AVERAGE DINNER FOR TWO: $65

Menu Highlights

Appetizers

White corn pancakes with Maine lobster & lobster sauce * Foie gras sautéed with arugula & Ported onions * Goat cheese & prawn tart with jalapeño sauce

Entrées

King salmon with basil & tomato * Roast squab with angel hair pasta & chanterelles * Roast lamb loin with rosemary & garlic served with apple-mint chutney

Maître d'
Rose Braun

Chef/Proprietor
Robert Kincaid

FRESH CREAM

100 HERITAGE HARBOR, SUITE F
NEAR FISHERMAN'S WHARF
MONTEREY, CA 93940
(408) 375-9798

Master Card & Visa Only
Closed Monday • Dinner Only

FRENCH

Just beyond the Monterey Wharf is the pale pink dining room of Fresh Cream, a mecca of fine French cuisine that seems miles from the bustling crowds.

Proprietor Robert Kincaid came to Monterey as a chef for the Hyatt Regency, fell in love with the region and decided to open a place of his own. Equipped with an old stove, some second-hand furniture and a lot of faith, he opened Fresh Cream on Cannery Row in 1980. Several years of hard work and word-of-mouth praise later, Fresh Cream was named second only to Masa's in a survey of *San Francisco Chronicle* readers' favorite restaurants.

Kincaid was able to move to spacious new quarters, where his restaurant continues to garner critical acclaim for its beautifully presented classical cuisine.

But the modest chef, who grows his own herbs, is just as dedicated as ever. "Sure I've achieved something," he says. "But I have to keep pushing myself to be the best that I can be." AVERAGE DINNER FOR TWO: $70

Menu Highlights

Appetizers
Artichoke bottoms with salmon quenelles ∗
Gratinée of mussels with almonds ∗ Fresh goose liver pâté

Entrées
Roasted rack of lamb for one ∗ Sautéed veal sweetbreads over four-color fresh pasta with black chanterelle mushrooms & cream ∗ Sautéed lobster & sea scallops with snow peas, shiitake mushrooms & sesame sauce

CONTINENTAL

THE GOLD FORK

OCEAN AVENUE
BETWEEN LINCOLN & DOLORES
CARMEL, CA 93921
(408) 624-2569

Major Credit Cards
Closed Monday · Dinner Only

☎ 🍸 ⅲ

General Manager
Russ Harris

Executive Chef
Ted Walter

With tapestries softening the stucco walls and a fire warming the hearth, The Gold Fork has a calm, welcoming ambiance most everyone finds irresistible.

Chef Ted Walter concerns himself with "the best use of the best ingredients," always searching for exciting combinations chosen for compatibility rather than sheer novelty. "Some chefs might try to startle diners with kiwi fruit on the magnificent swordfish I'm serving tonight," he explains. "I'm smoothing it with a paste of roasted eggplant and caramelized onion."

Manager Russ Harris calls The Gold Fork "a special occasion restaurant where you can dine elegantly and reasonably." He encourages "grazing," and even offers split meals for theatre-goers, suggesting they return after the curtain falls for dessert and coffee. But a superior wine list and an array of fine cognacs and armagnacs make it difficult to leave The Gold Fork, even for a few hours. AVERAGE DINNER FOR TWO: $60

Menu Highlights

Appetizers
Gold Fork trio of abalone, calamari puff & fried bufala mozzarella * Fresh artichoke bisque * Duck ravioli

Entrées
Tournedos Castroville with artichoke bottoms & mushroom crowns in Marsala & béarnaise sauce * Grilled veal chop Perigourdine * Cultured abalone

Proprietors
*Leonce Picot, Caroline Picot
& David Edgerton*

Chef
Emile Labrousse

FRENCH

The Old House

500 HARTNELL STREET
AT MADISON
MONTEREY, CA 93940
(408) 373-3737

Major Credit Cards
Open Daily • Dinner Only

Located in an adobe hut built when Monterey was still part of Mexico, The Old House harmonizes California's historic past with its exciting culinary present. The setting has the elegance of another age, yet the cuisine reflects the best of modern cooking.

Chef Emile Labrousse, a native of Perigord, France, has trained in Tours and worked both in Garmisch and at the famed La Mère Poulard in Mont-Saint-Michel. To that background, he brings what he describes as "California's bounty of gorgeous game, seafood and herbs."

Labrousse calls his specialty "real food: cooking for the fun of it." Flavors are authoritative; presentations are bright, but not contrived. And, unlike many restaurants of this type, The Old House serves substantial portions.

To keep the past alive, The Old House even has its own ghost, Hattie, who has gently made her presence known over the years. She is one more reason why this delightful restaurant is so unique. AVERAGE DINNER FOR TWO: $60

Menu Highlights

Appetizers
Castroville artichokes with blue crab *
Fetuccine with wild mushrooms * Hattie's
salad * Mustard prawns * Escargot salad

Entrées
Trout meunière with pinenuts &
mushrooms * Duck confit * Crab al pesto
* Poached or grilled Monterey Bay salmon

PACIFIC'S EDGE

HIGHLANDS INN
HIGHWAY ONE
CARMEL, CA 93921
(408) 624-3801

Major Credit Cards
Open Daily · Breakfast, Lunch & Dinner

Food & Beverage Director
David Fink

Chef
Don Ferch

Since 1916, the Highlands Inn has been a favorite destination for those traveling to the spectacular Carmel Highlands Coast. Now, with a complete renovation, it is as contemporary as it is historic.

The showpiece of that renovation is the Pacific's Edge, a glass-walled restaurant high on the cliff above the ocean. As entrancing as any that California has to offer, the views sweep the jagged coast and blue surf, framed by dark cypress and Monterey pines. Drawing on the produce of the area — fine local meats, seafood from the Monterey Bay, even seasonal mushrooms from the Big Sur forests — the menu is regional, fresh and creative every day.

The daily specials are spontaneous and explore the dazzling palette of contemporary cuisine. Complementing the California menu, the award-winning Pacific's Edge wine list focuses on the many outstanding wines of California, including those of the Monterey region. AVERAGE DINNER FOR TWO: $75

Menu Highlights

SEASONAL MENU

Appetizers

Cold tarragon-cured salmon with grilled brioche & caviar * Deep-fried calamari with roasted garlic * White bean soup with spicy sausage

Entrées

Grilled veal chop with Oregon morel mushrooms * Salmon sautéed with fennel, Roma tomatoes & tarragon * Sautéed Barbarie duck breast with wild rice cakes

The Queen of Chardonnay

La Reina

P.O. Box 1344 · Carmel, CA 408.649.0476

Proprietor
Remo d'Agliano

Chef/Proprietor
Amelia d'Agliano

ITALIAN

RAFFAELLO

MISSION STREET
BETWEEN OCEAN AND 7TH
CARMEL, CA 93921
(408) 624-1541

Major Credit Cards
Closed Tuesday • Dinner Only

In the style of great Florentine artisans and decorators, Remo d'Agliano and his wife, Danielle, have created an elegant dining room at Raffaello in picturesque Carmel-by-the-Sea. Beveled glass, etched with the fleur-de-lys of Florence, sets the keynote of the decor. Italian Copedemonte porcelain vases with fresh flowers decorate the reception room and each table of the moderately sized dining room.

Proprietor Remo d'Agliano grew up in Florence and apprenticed at his family's restaurant there. His formal training at the Culinary Academy of Paris broadened his style, adding a pinch of French seasoning to his Italian repertoire. His mother, Amelia d'Agliano, was chef at the family restaurant in Florence and, at seventy-four, is still in the kitchen today.

Mother and son, working in concert, prepare the homemade pasta, wine and cream sauces, scalloppine and a memorable *pollo alla Fiorentina.* AVERAGE DINNER FOR TWO: $50

Menu Highlights

Appetizers

Melon & prosciutto ∗ Smoked salmon ∗
Fetuccine alla Romana

Entrées

Duck with brandied orange sauce ∗
Fresh fish of the day: filet of sole
poached in Champagne with shrimp ∗
Chicken alla Fiorentina ∗ Monterey Bay
prawns with butter & garlic ∗ Veal
piccata with lemon sauce ∗ Sweetbreads
with cream & wine sauce

THE RIDGE

ROBLES DEL RIO LODGE
200 PUNTA DEL MONTE
CARMEL VALLEY, CA 93924
(408) 659-0170

Mastercard & Visa Only
Closed Monday · Lunch & Dinner · Sunday Brunch

Chef/Proprietor
Daniel Barduzzi

Executive Sous Chef
William Fogarty

High over the Carmel Valley, The Ridge combines spectacular views of the California countryside with an imaginative adaptation of classic country-French cuisine.

A native of Avignon, France, Chef/Proprietor Daniel Barduzzi is reluctant to give his cooking style a label. "Call it whatever you like," he says. "It's just good food." Still, a fine version of duck confit with real flageolet beans or a hearty cassoulet with fresh sausages from a local purveyor demonstrate his talent for presenting French dishes with California élan.

Chef Barduzzi combines the best of two worlds. No French cook ever used jalapeños the way he does to give a lift to broiled prawns, or shiitake mushrooms with chanterelles and domestic mushrooms to fill a puff pastry. Such originality is what makes the food at The Ridge as riveting as the views. AVERAGE DINNER FOR TWO: $50

Menu Highlights

Appetizers
Bourguignonne snails in new red potatoes
* Salad of smoked salmon, artichoke & goat cheese

Entrées
Braised sea bass with fresh fennel * Roast rack of lamb with mustard seed sauce * Duckling confit with green flageolets

ITALIAN

SARDINE FACTORY

701 WAVE STREET
ON CANNERY ROW
MONTEREY, CA 93940
(408) 373-3775

Major Credit Cards
Open Daily · Dinner Only

Proprietors
Ted Balestreri & Bert Cutino

Chef
Dan Catanio

The five grand dining areas that comprise The Sardine Factory are on a terrrace overlooking Monterey Bay. To the left of the entry is the cocktail lounge, where a 120-year-old hand-carved bar is the centerpiece. To the right is the original Captain's Dining Room, with fireplace, priceless oil paintings and numerous crystal chandeliers. Covered by a glass dome and surrounded by an enclosed garden, the Conservatory Room is dominated by a central crystal fountain statue, *The Birth of Venus*. The Wine Cellar dining room, medieval in decor, seats up to twenty-six people at a huge, hand-carved refectory table.

The wine and decor here are surpassed only by the bonhomie of proprietors Ted Balestreri and Bert Cutino. With Chef Dan Catanio, they have created an impres-

sive seafood menu with an Italian flair.

Their award-winning wine cellar offers a superb collection selected by one of America's top sommeliers, Frederick Dame. AVERAGE DINNER FOR TWO: $60

Menu Highlights

Appetizers

Linguine & shrimp Capri, sautéed in sweet butter & fresh basil * Spinach pasta triangles with Dungeness crabmeat in sundried-tomato beurre blanc

Entrées

Lamb Cotolette: oven-roasted lamb with fine herbs in Port sauce * Salmon Maltaise: filet of king salmon broiled on oakwood with a beurre blanc sauce

AMERICAN

SPYGLASS

LA PLAYA HOTEL
EIGHTH AVENUE & CAMINO REAL
CARMEL, CA 93921
(408) 624-4010

Major Credit Cards
Open Daily · Breakfast, Lunch & Dinner

General Manager
Tom Glidden

Chef
Cynthia Kaiser

Housed in the mission-style La Playa Hotel, which was built in 1906, the same year the village of Carmel-by-the-Sea was founded, The Spyglass recreates the atmosphere and hospitality of Old Carmel. Posters and artifacts from the early days of this artists' and writers' colony decorate the building, and the well-stocked antique carved walnut bar is a favorite gathering spot.

The dining area overlooks an enclosed city block of gorgeous secret gardens. Inside, the views are no less stunning. Chef Cynthia Kaiser's presentations are as beautiful and artistic as still lifes.

Proprietor Newton A. Cope, Jr., emphasizes that the culinary creations at the Spyglass are refinements of familiar American dishes. "Cynthia adds her own very inventive touches," he says, "but always as accents to basic, tasteful food."

Kaiser personally shops for the freshest tender baby vegetables, and cultivates the restaurant's herb garden on the hotel grounds. Many of the dishes are finished at the table for dramatic effect. AVERAGE DINNER FOR TWO: $55

Menu Highlights

Appetizers

Angel-hair pasta with fresh seafood * Pear & walnut salad with Roquefort * Smoked trout with horseradish cream * Baked brie with arugula

Entrées

Prawns Provencal with scallop souffle * Roast rack of lamb with Pommery mustard sauce * Cappellini with salmon, shrimp, roasted peppers & artichokes * Cioppino La Playa

POLO.
AS DEFINED
BY PIMM'S.

CHUKKER

Always preceded by Pimm's, i.e., Pimm's Chukker. A refreshing beverage served at polo matches and other smart places.

REGULATION GEAR

The Pimm's Cup. A cylindrical container open at one end with a capacity of 8 fluid ounces. Restricted to the sidelines.

THROW-IN

Throw 2 oz. Pimm's over ice. Fill with soda. Add a wedge of lemon. The Chukker begins.

BUMP

One-on-one contact of ice cubes. The angle of collision must be slight, causing no more than a clink.

THIRD MAN

The bartender.

GOAL

To make it to the Pimm's tent and back before the next chukker begins.

SAFETY

What you've reached when you make it back without spilling a precious drop.

FIELD

Anywhere. Anytime. Nowhere is out of bounds for a Pimm's Chukker.

TIME-OUT

What you should call if you run out of Pimm's Chukker.

HOOK

What we're offering to entice you into trying Pimm's. A set of 4 unbreakable Chukker cups. Write to: Pimm's "Cups" Offer, P.O. Box 3399, Young America, MN 55394. Send $1.50 check or money order. Void where prohibited.

**THE LIGHT REFRESHER FROM ENGLAND.
ONLY WINNING TASTES AS GOOD.**

CALIFORNIA WINES HAVE DEFINITELY COME OF AGE. The finest are now being collected, coveted and cellared with the zeal once reserved for prestigious European wines. Perhaps even more telling is the way the trendsetting restaurants of today, which once may have offered nothing but French wines, proudly offer an array of California wines.

European wine producers have in a way bestowed the ultimate compliment on California as a prime wine region. Many have chosen to become a part of the excitement. Companies such as Chandon, Piper, Bollinger, Roederer, Mouton-Rothschild, Antinori, Mumm, Freixenet and many others have joined the dynamic California wine world.

The number of wineries continues to expand as many small family-owned brands appear on the scene. With over 650 wineries in existence and more on the way, no winery will be able to rest on its laurels. This suggests that as good as California wines are today, the overall quality level will continue to rise.

WINES

BY NORMAN ROBY

The Best of California
VITICULTURAL AREAS

OF INTEREST TO MOST WINE CONSUMERS IS WHERE THE GRAPES WERE GROWN — IN OTHER words, the wine's origin. By January of 1983 the Treasury Department's Bureau of Alcohol, Tobacco and Firearms tightened the regulations governing place names. The growing region must be defined in terms of boundaries approved by the BATF. Now, when a name like Alexander Valley is used, at least 85 percent of the wine comes from that growing region. However, the winery itself does not have to be located within that region. The most widely seen place names are defined below.

• California

Still commonly used by both small and large producers, this designation means 100 percent of the wine came from vineyards within California.

• Napa Valley

Running thirty miles in length, this famous wine region keeps on getting bigger and better. Today, with close to 30,000 acres and about 150 wineries, Napa Valley is the clear-cut leader in wine quality and innovations. Leading wines are Chardonnay and Cabernet Sauvignon, but its reputation and future status hinge upon Cabernet Sauvignon — arguably the finest wine in the state.

• Sonoma & Mendocino County

These regions have been politically defined and adopted by the BATF. Seventy-five percent of the wine must come from the county.

• North Coast

This covers a wide range of vineyards in such diverse counties as Napa, Sonoma, Mendocino, Lake, Marin and Solano.

• Los Carneros District

One of the most visible viticultural areas, the Los Carneros District falls within both Napa and Sonoma counties. Close to San Francisco Bay, it is a cool growing area producing exquisite grapes. The region is becoming well known for its Pinot Noir and Chardonnay.

• Russian River Valley

This viticultural area follows the course of the Russian River and thus varies widely in its climate. The lower sector is a cool area preferred for its Chardonnay, Pinot Noir and sparkling wine varieties.

• Alexander Valley

Located in the inland northeast corner of Sonoma County, the Alexander Valley is large (12,000 acres) and relatively warm. It is quite versatile and has a reputation for rich Chardonnays and sought-after Cabernet Sauvignons.

• Sonoma Valley

Still known as the Valley of the Moon, this historic 5,000-acre region falls on the southwestern side of the Mayacamas mountain range, which separates it from the Napa Valley. Its wines are sought after by wine collectors.

• Central Coast

A large viticultural area, the Central Coast includes vineyards in the counties of Monterey, Santa Barbara, San Luis Obispo and San Benito.

• Sierra Foothills

Another multi-county place name, Sierra Foothills includes the historic Gold Rush regions of El Dorado, Amador and Calaveras counties.

• Temecula

Located between San Diego and Riverside County, this viticultural area is tempered by cool breezes and seems to excel in white varietals.

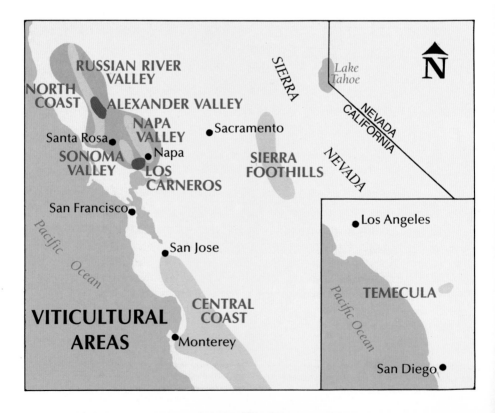

EVERYTHING PRINTED ON THE WINE LABEL FALLS UNDER THE CONTROL AND REGULATION OF THE BATF. All labels must be submitted for approval prior to usage. The government requires only the name of the producer (the brand), the type of wine (sparkling, table or fortified), and a statement of alcohol content. All other information on the front, back or neck labels is the marketing decision of the winery. The following are commonly used terms.

• Varietal Wine

Whenever the name of a grape variety appears on a label, from Chardonnay to Zinfandel, the wine must be made from at least 75 percent of the identified grape.

• Vintage Date

The year on the label is the year the grapes were harvested and the wine produced. U.S. regulations state that at least 95 percent of the wine's volume must come from grapes harvested in that vintage year.

• Alcohol by Volume

This is usually mentioned as a numerical percentage from 7 to 14 percent. The BATF allows a 1½ percent variance in either direction from the number that appears. An alternate way to state this requirement is "Table Wine."

• Produced & Bottled by

When this appears, it means the listed winery made (crushed and fermented) at least 75 percent of the wine in the bottle.

• Made & Bottled by

Though it sounds impressive, this phrase can be used if only 10 percent of the wine was made by the named brand. The rest could have been made by other wineries.

• Bottled by, Cellared by, Vinted by

This means the winery did little more than bottle the wine.

• Estate Bottled

This phrase can be used when the winery made all of the wine from vineyards it owns or when the winery has a long-term contract with the grape grower. Either way, the vineyards must be within the same area as the winery.

• Reserve, Private Reserve, Proprietor's Reserve

Presently no federal definition applies here, nor is there internal consensus among winemakers. The producer is implying the wine is special or the best of the vintage.

• Méthode Champenoise

On sparkling wine labels, this phrase means the wine was made by the traditional method followed in Champagne, France. The second fermentation occurs in the bottle, and the spent yeasts are later collected through riddling and removed through disgorging. This involves considerable labor and time.

• Cuvée

A blend of wines chosen by the winemaker, usually for making sparkling wine.

WINE TALK

PART OF THE ENJOYMENT OF WINES COMES FROM THE CONVERSATIONS THEY INSPIRE. QUITE often the subject is the wine itself. Talking about wine should be easy and relaxed. To help matters along, we have defined the most commonly used words and phrases, with particular emphasis on wine aromas. Most wine commentary proceeds by analogies and suggestions, so trust your instincts, offer your impressions and create descriptions.

• Aroma

All-purpose word for the smell of a wine, which may vary in type (fruity, floral, spicy) and in strength. Aroma is used in the general sense and is usually positive.

• Astringent

The sensation of a wine that leaves a puckery feel in the mouth and seems to dry out the palate. Most young Cabernets and Zinfandels are astringent. Tannins, from the grapes and oak barrels, contribute to astringency, which is more common in red wines.

• Austere

Characteristic of wines that are lean in body and high in acidity but overall on the pleasant side. Usually white wines are likely to be austere in style.

• Balanced

When all of a wine's components (fruit, alcohol, acidity, tannin, oak, sweetness) exist in a harmonious way, the wine is said to be balanced.

• Berry-Like

Common aroma description for wines with fairly distinct fruit character. Zinfandels are often similar to blackberries, Cabernets to black currants and Pinot Noirs to cherries.

• Body

The relative weight of a wine or its viscosity. Ranges from thin to light, to medium, to full-bodied. Swirling your wine in the glass and noting how it clings to the sides is an indication of its viscosity.

• Bouquet

The odors developed through the vinification process as distinguished from the fruity/spicy aroma of the grape.

• Complex

Describes both aromas and flavors, and the existence of several facets simultaneously. Multi-dimensional wines are complex. The opposite style is simple or one-dimensional.

• Crisp

Wines that are lively on the palate and leave you with a lip-smacking impression similar to tart. Usually results from relatively high acidity.

• Dry

Basically, the opposite of sweet.

• Earthy

Exists in varying degrees, from a subtle aroma of dusty weediness to a pungent aroma of mushrooms and truffles. More commonly found in red wines.

• Floral

Aromas similar to flowers in bloom are said to be floral. White wines such as Johannisberg Riesling and Gewurztraminer are often floral with hints of jasmine and orange blossom. The aroma of violets and roses exists in some Pinot Noirs.

• Grassy

A fresh, lively aroma reminiscent of freshly cut grass or new-mown hay, usually considered pleasant, and characteristic of many Sauvignon Blancs. Some Chardonnays and a few Chenin Blancs can be grassy.

• Herbaceous/Herbal

Collective terms for aromas hinting of dried herbs such as sage, dill and mint. Herbaceousness is most often found in Sauvignon Blanc.

• Honey

An enticing sweet smell present in some white wines. It is usually a result of Botrytis cinerea, "the noble rot."

• Intense

An impression of richness and depth of flavor. Powerful in character.

• Mature

Wines that have reached their peak development and are said to be at their optimum stage for drinking.

• Nose

The combination of all odors, aroma, bouquet, oak, etc., detected by your olfactory sense.

• Oaked

The aroma derived directly from oak barrel aging and usually described as vanilla-like. The oak is fired to conform to the barrel shape.

• Smoky

An aroma derived mostly from fired oak barrels and often perceived as toasty or roasted, similar to the smell of burning leaves.

• Spicy

Many fine wines are characteristically spicy, suggesting cloves, cinnamon and pepper. Zinfandel and Syrah wines tend to be peppery; among white wines, Gewurztraminer can be very spicy.

• Supple

A wine that is extremely subtle in a soft, smooth style without being heavy in body.

• Tannic

A rough, mouth-drying quality found in the aftertaste of many new red wines. Tannins come from the skins of grapes and from wood barrels. This flavor softens with time; the amount of tannin helps determine a wine's aging requirements.

• Vegetative

This covers a range of aromas, from the quite attractive smell of green olives and bell peppers often common to Cabernet Sauvignon and Sauvignon Blanc, to the less attractive green bean and asparagus smells sometimes detected in both types of wine.

• Yeasty

The aroma similar to that of fresh-baked bread, which is highly desirable in Champagne and sparkling wines. Some white wines, notably Chardonnay and Sauvignon Blanc, are aged in contact with yeast and acquire subtle yeastiness.

FROM
CÔTE-TO-COAST
BOUCHARD PÈRE & FILS

Domaines du Château de Beaune

Beaune du Château *Premier Cru*

*Beaune *"Clos de la Mousse"*

*Beaune *"Clos Saint-Landry"*

*Beaune-Grèves *Vigne de L'Enfant Jésus*

Beaune-*"Marconnets"*

Beaune-*"Teurons"*

Chambertin

Chambolle-Musigny

Chevalier-Montrachet

Corton-Charlemagne

Le Corton

Meursault-*"Genevrières"*

Montrachet

Pommard *Premier Cru*

Savigny-Les-Beaune *"Les Lavières"*

Volnay-*"Caillerets"*

Volnay-*"Chanlin"*

*Volnay-Fremiets *"Clos de la Rougeotte"*

Volnay-*"Taillepieds"*

*Fine Burgundy and Rhône Wines
from Bouchard Père Et Fils*

"Le Chamville" Beaujolais-Villages

"Le Chamville" Macon-Villages

*Château De La Font Du Loupe
Châteauneuf-du-Pape

*Depuis 1731 - Au Château -
Beaune - Côte-D'Or - France*

*Sole Proprietor

A New Vision

The essence of Napa Valley's finest vineyards and California's innovative winemaking style, captured in the classic tradition of France.

Mumm Cuvée Napa

*A*lthough technically only French sparkling wines can be called Champagnes, some California producers do use the term. Either way, California now makes millions of bottles of this delicious, bubbly wine, ready to be enjoyed on any occasion. The finest are produced by the *méthode champenoise*, the traditional, labor-intensive system required of all French Champagnes. Labor-saving methods generally result in less satisfying flavors. The combination of fruitiness and yeastiness that is characteristic of California sparkling wines gives them a more youthful style than those from France.

SPARKLING WINES

NORMAN ROBY ✸ RECOMMENDS

Domaine Chandon: *Part of the Moet-Hennessy firm, Chandon has a first-class operation, from its vinification to its restaurant. The Reserve Brut is one of the finest sparkling wines produced in California.*

Domaine Mumm: *A joint venture of France's G.H. Mumm and Seagram's Classics, Domaine Mumm's Cuvée Napa Brut is a winner. It's a sparkling wine with a pale bronze-copper color and a balance of fruit and toasty yeast.*

Gloria Ferrer: *Owned by the Freixenet Company of Spain, this spectacular winery is in the Carneros region of Sonoma. It has built a solid reputation for its Brut, and has a delicate vintage sparkler, the Brut Royal Cuvée.*

Iron Horse Vineyards: *From its own vineyards in cool Sonoma, Iron Horse makes a modest number of impressive sparkling wines.*

Robert Hunter: *Vineyardist Robert Hunter joins forces with Dan Duckhorn in this sparkling wine. The Brut de Noirs, made from Pinot Noir, is sophisticated, yeasty and dry.*

Maison Deutz: *Another French-owned California venture, Deutz set* up camp in San Luis Obispo. Their sparkling wine is complex and exciting, made from Chardonnay and Pinot Blanc.

Piper-Sonoma: *Piper-Heidsieck's winery uses Sonoma County grapes for its popular Brut. The long-aged Tête de Cuvée is handsome, but the finest overall wine is the delightful Blanc de Noirs.*

Schramsberg Vineyards: *In 1965 Jack Davies boldly decided to make high-quality sparkling wine in the Napa Valley. Perseverance pays, as Schramsberg is still one of the best.*

Michael Tribaut: *Two French winemakers produce exceptional sparkling wines from Monterey County grapes. The Brut, unusual but tasty, is made of Pinot Noir and Chardonnay.*

Château St. Jean: *With the 1983 and '84 vintages, Château St. Jean proved what it could do with sparkling wines. Both the Brut and Blanc de Blancs are beautifully balanced.*

Scharffenberger: *Using grapes from the cool Anderson Valley, a region coming to life for sparkling wine, Scharffenberger has shown the way in quality sparkling wines since 1984.*

The search for a light-bodied, refreshing, lively white wine often ends with Chenin Blanc. This enormously pleasing varietal was restyled in the 1950s by the Charles Krug Winery to the present slightly sweet rendition. Most winemakers emphasize the grape's freshness and forthright melon-peach aroma, while retaining its slight sweetness for balance and length of flavor. Though over 45,000 acres of Chenin Blanc are planted, much of the land is earmarked for upgrading inexpensive jug wines. Quality Sonoma County producers value Chenin Blanc for its adaptability to the trend toward lower-alcohol wine.

CHENIN BLANC

NORMAN ROBY 💥 RECOMMENDS

Grand Cru Vineyards: *In 1981 winemaker Bob Magnani and proprietor Walt Dryer experimented with some Chenin Blanc from Cook Vineyards in the Delta Region. Others now emulate their lively, low-alcohol wine.*

Simi Winery: *Every year since 1982, Simi's subtle, slightly sweet Chenin Blanc is the finest in its style. The combination of fruit and refreshing acidity makes it a super choice with many appetizers.*

Chalone Vineyards: *As one of the first great small wineries, Chalone defined a style of winemaking that favors richness and powerful flavors. Often its Chenin Blanc is confused with Chardonnay because of its depth.*

Chappellet Vineyards: *Don and Molly Chappellet have never wavered in their belief that a fuller-bodied, dry, lightly oaked Chenin Blanc will be appreciated. Restaurant sales provide positive proof.*

Charles Krug Winery: *With a new label and renewed commitment, the Krug Winery is once again producing fine Chenin Blancs. The 1986 launched the comeback.*

Fetzer Vineyards: *As annual production moves toward the million-*

case mark, the Fetzer family continues to offer high-quality wines of all types. The Chenin Blanc is lively and among the best in a low-alcohol style.

Guenoc Winery: *On an estate once owned by Lily Langtry, Guenoc has helped revive Lake County as a wine-growing region through consistent vintages of dry, rich, refined Chenin Blanc.*

Girard Winery: *From their compact, modern winery off Napa Valley's Silverado Trail, owner Steve Girard and winemaker Fred Payne make a rich Chenin Blanc, with light oak flavors and great balance.*

Villa Mt. Eden: *One of only a few Napa wineries still interested in Chenin Blanc, Villa Mt. Eden brings out more flavor and richness than any other producer. With attractive aromas of peaches and pears, this Chenin Blanc reminds some experts of Chardonnay.*

Pine Ridge Winery: *The light color of this Chenin Blanc doesn't prepare you for its fruitiness, lively flavors and honey-like aftertaste, all typical of the Pine Ridge style. The wine is on the sweet side, but served chilled, it is highly versatile.*

Classic Artistry.
Reserve Chardonnay by William Hill.

Robert Pepi Winery we make wines to share with friends, to accompany grand meals,
seal a promise or a new beginning, or to celebrate a milestone in life. Sometimes a great
moment is just the realization that you got through a tough day with flying colors.

THE WINE OF CHOICE.

ROBERT PEPI
NAPA VALLEY, CALIFORNIA

$\mathcal{R}$obert Mondavi single-handedly removed Sauvignon Blanc from the endangered species list in 1967 by christening his version Fumé Blanc. That established the trend toward dry, lightly oak-aged, medium-bodied, crisp white wines. Labeled either Fumé Blanc or Sauvignon Blanc—the names are interchangeable—the wines range in character from an intense aroma of bell peppers and green peas to a subdued fragrance of figs and freshly cut grass. Between light Chenin Blancs and fuller-bodied Chardonnays, Sauvignon (Fumé) Blancs are natural choices for restaurant consumption.

Sauvignon Blanc & Fume Blanc

NORMAN ROBY ✸ RECOMMENDS

Kenwood Vineyards: *Twins Mike and Marty Lee helped transform an old Sonoma Valley winery into a quality wine-producing facility. Since 1982, outstanding Sauvignon Blancs have secured its reputation.*

Ferrari-Carano Winery: *Don and Rhonda Carano have designed a fantastic winery complex complete with Italian-style villa. They have not ignored their wines: the Fumé Blanc is rich, well-knit and stylish.*

Robert Mondavi Winery: *The Mondavis continue to fine-tune Fumé Blanc while maintaining high standards. The style is moderately grassy, lightly oaked and well-balanced.*

Château St. Jean: *Winemaker Dick Arrowood isolates the best vineyards in Sonoma County and captures the individuality of each. His La Petite Etoile is bold, pungent and snappy; the estate-grown St. Jean Vineyard is rich with mouth-watering fruitiness.*

Matanzas Creek Winery: *Winemaker David Ramey favors light oak touches to add richness to his long-lived Sauvignon Blancs. For several consecutive vintages, they have topped the list of oak barrel-influenced Sauvignons.*

Cakebread Cellars: *Well-known photographer Jack Cakebread loves big, rich, imposing Sauvignon Blancs. Recent vintages are among the largest and best.*

Dry Creek Vineyard: *The assertive, grassy, herbaceous 1985 Fumé Blanc is in the classic varietal style upon which winemaker David Stare has built his good name. The 1986 release has a similar hint of vanilla. Dry Creek is a popular growing area for this varietal.*

Frogs Leap: *A new (1981) and modest (2,500 cases) winery leaped into everyone's heart with an artistically graceful label and an equally refined varietal. Lemon, lilac, bell pepper and sweet French oak scents and flavors are combined in each vintage for a wonderfully silky, dry wine.*

Husch Vineyards: *A model of consistency for years, Husch cranks out a sprightly Sauvignon Blanc made from grapes grown on its own "La Ribera Vineyard" in Mendocino County. The winery is in Philo.*

Hanna Winery: *It was hard to compete with the unique, colorful label, but the wines have been equal to the task. Excellent varietal character combines with unusual depth of flavor in this age-worthy version.*

SAUVIGNON BLANC & FUMÉ BLANC

NORMAN ROBY ✹ RECOMMENDS

Sterling Vineyards: With each vintage, winemaker Bill Dyer fine-tunes his wines. The latest vintages of Sauvignon Blanc favor youthful appeal, freshness and delightfully subtle oak touches.

Beaulieu Vineyard: In 1985 this longtime producer of Sauvignon Blanc switched to a lighter, more contemporary style, which was an overnight success. The current vintage has the same forthright appeal.

Robert Pecota Winery: The label says "Barrel Fermented" to hint at the depth, complexity and rich texture of Pecota's style. The oak is evident but unobtrusive. This could be one to cellar for a few years.

Buena Vista Winery: Although well established in Sonoma, with acreage in the Carneros region, the winery loves what Lake County offers in Sauvignon Blanc. The result is a superb, lemony, light-bodied refresher.

Robert Pepi Winery: After establishing a strong reputation as Napa Valley grape growers, Robert Pepi and son built a winery in Oakville in 1981. They have since built a fine reputation for Sauvignon Blanc in a medium-bodied, well-balanced style.

Iron Horse: From its estate-grown Alexander Valley grapes, Iron Horse specializes in streamlined, subtle, slightly oaked Fumé Blancs.

Honig Winery: Specializing in Sauvignon Blanc only, educator Bill Honig's winery prefers 100 percent varietal composition and a hint of oak flavor. The wine is medium bodied and sturdy.

Carmenet: With a good percentage of Semillon, Carmenet's Sauvignon Blanc combines lovely varietal fruit with a creamy, soft texture.

Grand Cru Vineyards: Winemaker Bob Nagani puts as much flavor and character into Sauvignon Blanc as anyone. Though rich and complex, these wines are not overly oaked and can be enjoyed in their youth.

McDowell Valley Vineyards: This Mendocino County producer offers an Estate Bottled Fumé Blanc that is round, smooth and versatile. Its character tends toward refinement.

Creston Manor: A spectacular new winery in San Luis Obispo County, Creston Manor has proven to be adept at making a rich, creamy style of barrel-fermented Sauvignon Blanc.

Beaulieu Vineyard

**THE PRIVATE
COLLECTOR'S
PRIVATE
RESERVE™**

To Send a Gift of Beaulieu Vineyard, Call 1-800-272-5883

Beaulieu Vineyard, Rutherford, Napa Valley, California - USA

Was it this one of a kind etched bottle that aroused everyone's imagination at the Napa Valley wine auction or was it the combination of our estate vineyards, total dedication to quality and a Cabernet from the winery's centennial year?

Implicit in the winning bid of $12,000 was the confirmation of an important message: The vintners of Napa Valley are producing wines acknowledged to be on a par with the finest in the world.

Join us in a toast to those who have provided such a rich history and such a bright future.

Far Niente
A Napa Valley Wine Estate

This 9.0 liter bottle of Far Niente's 1985 Cabernet sold at this years Napa Valley Wine Auction for $12,000.00, the highest price ever for a single bottle of Napa Valley wine.

*C*hardonnay is without question the richest and most complex-tasting white wine. Since the early 1970s, when California Chardonnays began attracting international recognition, the number of first-rate Chardonnays has increased dramatically. The prevailing character of Chardonnay is a spiced apple, ripe apricot aroma in a medium-bodied to medium-full-bodied style. The subtle individual differences in style depend upon the degree of oak-aging and the regional character imposed by the climate and soil.

CHARDONNAY

NORMAN ROBY ✸ RECOMMENDS

Matanzas Creek Winery: *Located in the pastoral Bennett Valley of Sonoma County, this modest winery (5,000 cases) quickly rose to the top with impeccably made, rich and balanced Chardonnays.*

Grgich Hills Cellars: *Mike Grgich made a reputation for himself at Château Montelena (1972-1976), then continued to make top-notch Chardonnays at his winery. "Hills" refers to Austin Hills of the coffee family.*

Château Montelena: *With young winemaker Bo Barrett at the helm, Montelena maintains its fine record with its Alexander Valley and Napa Valley Chardonnays. This 100-year-old stone castle winery makes an ideal stopover.*

Château St. Jean: *Beginning in 1974, St. Jean has made Chardonnays from over a dozen individual vineyards in Sonoma County. Robert Young and Belle Terre Vineyards have made the winery famous. The vintages of winemaker Richard Arrowood age beautifully.*

Acacia Winery: *Though better known for Pinot Noir, Acacia offers several rich, lush and well-oaked Chardonnays. The favorites are the Carneros and Winery Lake Vineyard versions, both textured, long-finish wines.*

William Hill Winery: *William Hill produces two styles of Chardonnay. The Gold Label is slightly buttery, oak-aged, assertive and complex, elegant with food. The Silver Label is lighter, with lively fruit freshness and finesse.*

Chalone: *One of the first to make great Chardonnays, Chalone maintains its fine record. The Chardonnays are intensely flavored, built to last, and worthy of a special search. Since Chalone has increased its production, availability is less of a problem.*

Sequoia Grove Vineyards: *This small winery in the Central Napa Valley has been making steady progress up the Chardonnay ladder. The Allen family seems to prefer a fairly aggressive Chardonnay style, but they round it off with ample oak character for one of the best-kept secrets around.*

Kendall Jackson Vineyards: *This Lake County winery's winemaker, Jed Steele, prefers to blend grapes from several locations for his balanced, refined Chardonnays. The Vintner's Reserve offers character and charm for a modest price. Those seeking rich, massive style will like Steele's Proprietor's Reserve.*

Pine Ridge Winery: *As this winery expands production, the quality of its wine continues to improve. Winemaker Gary Andrus hit a hot streak with his 1983 Chardonnays: the Knollside Cuvée has a superb structure.*

Kistler Vineyards: *Kistler began its career with a fantastic 1979 Chardonnay, then dropped back into the crowd until recently. The 1985 Chardonnays once again demonstrate the craftmanship of winemaker Mark Bixler.* ·

Clos du Bois: *The Alexander Valley Proprietary Reserve, golden in color with an apricot and vanilla nose, has complexity and wonderful balance.*

Cuvaison Winery: *Using grapes from the Carneros district, Swiss owners and winemaker John Thacher have brought recent Chardonnay vintages to the top. The wine is buttery, full flavored and intricately balanced.*

Dry Creek Vineyards: *One of the unsung heroes of Chardonnay, owner David Stare was a modern pioneer in Sonoma County winemaking. In the 1980s his Chardonnays have been superbly crafted and affordable.*

ZD Wines: *ZD has produced so many outstanding Chardonnays that one can only wonder why it is not famous. Owner Norm De Leuze and his winemaker brother Robert seem to prefer their wines to speak for themselves. Their Chardonnays are rich, creamy, oaky and just plain beautiful.*

Silverado Vineyards: *Winemaker Jack Stuart has a knack for making luscious fruit Chardonnays so appeal-* *ing when new that they rapidly disappear from wine lists. They are, however, serious wines.*

Ventana Vineyards: *Winemaker Doug Meador makes a big, full-bodied, beautifully oaked Chardonnay that is a champion on any table. His Ventana Vineyards produce grapes sought after by many other wineries.*

Edna Valley: *From the coolest regions of San Luis Obispo County, the winery creates rich, barrel-fermented, butterscotch-flavored Chardonnays, which are among the most intensely flavored produced anywhere.*

St. Clement Vineyards: *Winemaker Dennis Johns blends selected lots of Napa Valley grapes to create a well-proportioned, rich-tasting Chardonnay.*

Simi Winery: *Using grapes from Mendocino and Sonoma counties in a creative blend, winemaker Zelma Long is a supreme stylist. Her Chardonnays capture fruitiness and oak complexity in a silky, medium-bodied wine.*

Monticello Cellars: *Owner Jay Corley is a Thomas Jefferson scholar, which explains the winery's name. He also appreciates artistic efforts in wines and has found a winemaker, Allan Philips, who can do just about anything. The Chardonnays combine wonderful fruit, medium oak and a balance of crisp acidity.*

Beaulieu Vineyards: *One of the first to plant grapes in the Carneros area, Beaulieu produces a super Chardonnay — the leader of their Carneros wines.*

CHARDONNAY

Beringer Vineyards: *Since the mid-1970s, the quality of Beringer wines has followed an upward chart. Its Napa Valley Chardonnay could well be the best value around, since it has the depth of flavor usually found at double the price.*

DeLoach Vineyards: *Former San Francisco fireman Cecil DeLoach has proven to be adept at just about every wine he makes, but since 1982 his Chardonnays have been particularly stunning.*

Fetzer Vineyards: *Of the many wines that the Fetzer family makes well, the Barrel Select Chardonnay could possibly be the standout. Its complex fruit flavors with substantial oak nuances are being discovered by wine lovers around the country.*

Freemark Abbey: *This winery's fame for Cabernet Sauvignon may have overshadowed its achievement with Chardonnay. The winery favors a smooth style and a lively apple aroma with a hint of background oak. The vintages age surprisingly well.*

Sterling Vineyards: *It may be difficult to figure out which Sterling wine is best, but the winery has certainly come a long way with Chardonnay. It now makes two standouts: the long-aged, mountain-grown Diamond Mountain Ranch, and the medium-bodied, beautiful Napa Valley version.*

Trefethen Vineyards: *Since 1977, the Trefethens have perfected a rather subtle style of Chardonnay. Made from locally grown grapes, their Chardonnay offers refined apple and spice flavors with a light oak character. Slow to develop, but long lasting, Trefethen Chardonnay is consistently good.*

Sonoma-Cutrer: *Well-known winemaker Bill Bonetti helped design the high-tech winery that enables him to specialize in exciting Chardonnays. The Russian River Ranches has a youthful appeal, while the Cutrer bottling is richer and more complex. The Les Pierres version is delicious.*

Hacienda: *Recent vintages of the Clair de Lune Chardonnay have demonstrated superb winemaking in a mildly oaked style. The 1986 is particularly good.*

Raymond Vineyards: *Well known in Napa wine circles, the Raymonds have been involved in grape growing and winemaking for decades. All Raymond wines are good, but recent vintages of their rich, fruity and nicely structured Chardonnay have been standouts in both quality and value.*

La Reina: *This small winery specializes in barrel-fermented, richly flavored Chardonnays. They show Monterey County character at its best.*

Shafer: *Well known for their Cabernets, Shafer recently established a fine reputation for Chardonnay. Winemaker Doug Shafer is particularly proud of his 1982 vintage, since that was a difficult growing year.*

Mazzocco Vineyards: *Two lively, fruity Chardonnays are made by this small Sonoma winery, a barrel-fermented Sonoma County Chardonnay and an estate grown River Lane Chardonnay from the Alexander Valley.*

THE
ACCENT
IS ON
TASTE.

$\mathcal{A}$'s pronounced in character as it is difficult to pronounce, Gewurztraminer has developed a strong following among restaurant-goers. "Gewurz" means spicy and seasoned in German; with its orange-blossom and lychee-nut aroma, Gewurztraminer complements hot, spicy and Oriental-style cuisines. The grape, which came to California from northern Italy and French Alsace, demands a cool climate and exceptional winemaking talents. Because it tends to be slightly bitter, most winemakers prefer to soften and smooth it with subtle sweetness.

GEWURZTRAMINER

NORMAN ROBY ✹ RECOMMENDS

Joseph Phelps Vineyards: *Year in, year out, the Phelps style captures full fragrance in a rich, balanced presentation.*

Grand Cru Vineyards: *Full-flavored, with an opulent aroma and a definite sweet edge, Grand Cru's version is spicy. Proprietor Walt Dryer and winemaker Bob Magnani have amassed an impressive record.*

Navarro Vineyards: *From grapes grown in the cool Anderson Valley of Mendocino County, Navarro makes a firm, strong and definitely dry style wine. It reminds many of the Alsatian Gewurztraminer.*

Mark West Vineyards: *From Joan and Bob Ellis's low-profile winery in the Russian River Valley of Sonoma comes a crisp style of refined, balanced and surprisingly long-lived Gewurztraminers.*

Hacienda Winery: *Emphasizing an opulent aroma and depth, Hacienda captures strong definition. Its Gewurztraminer stands up to the most powerful foods.*

Lazy Creek Vineyards: *Located in Mendocino's Anderson Valley, this small winery is gaining a reputation for a fragrant, well-defined Gewurztraminer, perfect with spicy food.*

Fetzer Vineyards: *Year in and year out, the Fetzers perform minor miracles with this difficult varietal. Fetzer's style leans toward sweetness and has a soft, generous appeal that makes it ideal as an apéritif wine.*

Monticello Cellars: *With vineyards in the cooler, southern portion of Napa Valley, Monticello built its early reputation on Gewurztraminer. Although Jay Corley has since expanded his list of achievements in the wine world, his dry-style Gewurztraminer remains one of the finest and most popular.*

Gundlach-Bundschu Winery: *A favorite of the Bundschu family, this wine is a fine example of forthright, lively floral character. It has a surprising degree of flavor for a lighter-bodied Gewurztraminer.*

Château St. Jean: *Extremely fruity and moderately spicy, St. Jean's wines are lighter in body, with vibrant flavors. Short aging brings them to a lovely peak.*

J. Pedroncelli Winery: *The Pedroncelli family has been making wine since 1927, and today, Jim and John are highly regarded for their medium-dry, spicy Gewurztraminer. Its citrus aroma, apricot-like taste and clean finish make it an ideal accompaniment to spicy cuisine.*

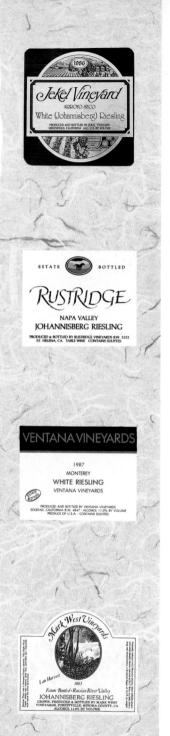

*R*egarded worldwide as one of the select noble grape varieties, Johannisberg Riesling yields one of the most delicate and subtle of all white wines. Simply called Riesling in its German homeland, it is usually labeled Johannisberg or White Riesling in California. Known today as a tough sell among producers, Johannisberg Riesling suffers from an association with sweet wines. Among the well-made ones, the sweetness level is low and only part of the overall appeal. To counter the image, a few wineries bottle an Early Harvest version in which crisp acidity balances any overt sweetness.

JOHANNISBERG RIESLING

Jekel Vineyard: *As a pioneer in Monterey County, Jekel made an early impact with its Rieslings, which remain among the more enticing, opulently scented and perfectly balanced versions produced.*

Firestone Vineyard: *Owned by Brooks Firestone of the tire company and Suntory of Japan, the Firestone Vineyard is located in the Santa Ynez Valley. Its Rieslings are floral and refreshing.*

Clos du Bois: *The Early Harvest style of Riesling with low alcohol and high, refreshing acidity is rendered in a lovely way by this Sonoma County winery.*

Trefethen Vineyards: *Labeled White Riesling, its wines are among the best made in Napa Valley and among the least sweet of those produced in California. The style is delicate, but holds up well with main courses.*

Freemark Abbey Winery: *Long established in Napa, Freemark Abbey has probably enjoyed more success with Riesling than any other winery in California. Vintages in the 1980s have offered genuine fresh blossom aromas in a slightly sweet style. A perfect refreshment wine.*

Joseph Phelps Vineyards: *Among several Rieslings made each year, the Early Harvest has fine character and sufficient flavor interest to accompany rather spicy food. Joe Phelps has always shown personal interest in the Riesling varietal.*

Geyser Peak Winery: *By bottling quality wine at more than reasonable prices, Geyser Peak has won many fans. Strong on character, the "Soft" Riesling is among its finest wines.*

Rust Ridge: *This small Napa winery specializes in Rieslings made in an elegant, floral style that is surprisingly versatile.*

Callaway Vineyard: *Just about every wine from this white wine specialist offers good value. Its White Riesling might be the best, most distinctive varietal for the money. It is light in style, refreshing and suitable as a sophisticated sipping wine.*

Ventana Vineyards: *Owner Doug Meador is a leader in grape growing in northern Monterey County. His specialty is white varietal wine, well represented by Ventana's White Riesling, an excellent choice as an apéritif or with cracked crab.*

A REPUTATION
GOOD AS GOLD

Next time, you be the judge.
Discover the quality that has
made us the most award winni...
vineyard in America.

VENTANA VINEYARDS

As professional wine tasters in France, we had the pleasure of evaluating over 2,000 California wines.

Now owners of Chateau Potelle in Napa Valley, we are proud to be making California wines with a French accent ... elegant wines that respect the unique personality nature has given these grapes.

Bon Appétit!

Jean-Noel and Marketta Fourmeaux du Sartel

CHATEAU POTELLE
NAPA VALLEY

The California Wines with a French Accent

$\mathcal{P}$inot Noir has come a long way in recent years. Then again, this red varietal wine had plenty of room for improvement. Only winemakers interested in and committed to Pinot Noir located the ideal sites for growing this temperamental, finicky grape. Textbook Pinot Noirs capture a spicy cinnamon and wild-cherry aroma and offer a smooth-as-satin texture. The color tends to be lighter than most red wines and may even show a brown tint. Los Carneros District (located in both Napa and Sonoma counties), Russian River Valley, Monterey and Sonoma Valley are the premier appellations.

NORMAN ROBY ✸ RECOMMENDS

Dehlinger Winery: *Over several vintages, this Russian River Valley family winery went from obscurity to fame on the basis of its red wines. The Pinot Noirs are rich, with ripe fruit flavors balanced by tannins.*

Acacia Winery: *A new kid ensconced in the Carneros area, Acacia set out to make great Pinot Noir. It follows the French approach by isolating individual vineyards and makes five different, fruity, toasted-oak versions.*

Calera Wines: *Owner Josh Jensen searched everywhere before locating vineyards rich in chalk and limestone along a mountain range in Monterey County's Gavilan Range. From his three small vineyards — Jensen, Selleck and Reed — he makes intense Pinot Noirs.*

Saintsbury Cellars: *Since 1980, Saintsbury Pinot Noirs have been acclaimed as pure and lovely versions. Made from Carneros-grown fruit, they capture the wild-cherry, satiny-smooth character of the grape.*

Chalone Vineyards: *While the 1969 Chalone Pinot Noir remains legendary, Chalone's recent vintages have been only slightly less spectacular.*

Carneros Creek Winery: *Since the 1976 vintage, this winery has led the turnabout in Pinot Noir's reputation with an experimental vineyard to isolate the best vines and improve growing methods. The resulting wines have been exciting.*

La Crema: *Once known as La Crema Vinera, the winery changed names to reflect change of ownership and style. The Pinot Noir is poised and redolent of black cherries and spice.*

Sanford Winery: *Richard Sanford loves to make fairly big, complex Pinot Noirs from Central Coast fruit. His Pinots age well.*

Gundlach-Bundschu Winery: *From grapes grown in the family's Carneros vineyards, this winery produces a Pinot Noir that is cherry-like and fruity. The 1985 vintage introduced a more elegant style.*

Navarro Vineyards: *Here's a small winery enjoying a cult following for its Pinot Noirs. Located in Anderson Valley, Navarro makes Pinots with spice and depth.*

David Bruce Winery: *A pioneer of Pinot Noir since the late 1960s, David Bruce makes a rich style of wine in the Santa Cruz mountains.*

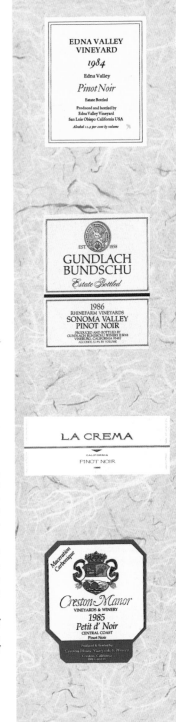

...*enjoyed*
at the finest restaurants.

CUVAISON

Chardonnay

Napa Valley

1987

ALC. 13.0% BY VOL.

4550 SILVERADO TRAIL, P.O. BOX 384, CALISTOGA, CA 94515 (707) 942-6266 TELEX: 176877 FAX: (707) 942-57.

$\mathcal{T}$he greatest success story of the late 1970s, Merlot has emerged from relative obscurity to rival Cabernet Sauvignon as the preferred full-flavored red wine. The Louis M. Martini Winery made California's first varietal Merlot in 1968; Sterling Vineyards made the second in 1969. Now every winery with access to Merlot grapes produces one. Merlot's central appeal resides in aromas similar to Cabernet —black currants, black cherries and herbs—but with a softness and smoothness all its own.

MERLOT

NORMAN ROBY ✸ RECOMMENDS

Duckhorn Vineyards: *Winemaker Tony Rinaldi combines ripe, rich fruit with just the right level of sweet oak to come up with top-notch Merlots, leaders since 1978. Both the Three Palms Vineyard and the Napa Valley are usually super.*

Matanzas Creek Vineyard: *Though Matanzas Creek produces many excellent wines, it wants to be known in the future for Merlot. Over the last few vintages, its Merlots have been so concentrated in varietal flavor and overall complexity that the future is now.*

Newton Vineyard: *Within only a few vintages, Newton has soared to the top of the Merlot division. Lovely and built to last, the Merlots contain Cabernet Franc, which adds complexity to the fragrance.*

Vichon: *Owned and operated by Robert Mondavi's three children, Vichon has added a terrific Merlot to the family's output. A ripe cherry aroma combines with a round, smooth texture for a tantalizing wine.*

Sterling Vineyard: *Started by Peter Newton in 1968, the winery is now part of the Seagram group. Soft and supple, the finer vintages peak five to six years after harvest.*

Cuvaison Winery: *An instant critical success, the first vintage sold out, and the next was a voluptuous follow-up. Cuvaison is a name to remember if you love full-flavored Merlots.*

Franciscan Vineyards: *Agustin Huneeus is at the helm of this Napa Valley winery, indicative of his commitment to excellence. A leading producer of Merlot, Franciscan's version is deep garnet with smoky cassis, oaky and varietal aromas and a good balance of acids and tannins.*

Markham Vineyards: *Still a sleeper despite recent vintage successes, Markham offers some of the most enticing, multi-faceted Merlots around. Capable of a long life, they are also delightful when young.*

St. Francis Winery: *Owner Joe Martin is a big, friendly guy, and his Merlots happen to be powerful yet very pleasant, full-flavored and perfectly balanced by strong American oak notes.*

Lakespring Winery: *With its high standards, Lakespring frequently excels with Merlot. Winemaker Randy Mason leans toward a medium-bodied, streamlined style for a wine that is spicy, herbal and always youthfully accessible.*

MERLOT

Rutherford Hill Winery: *One of the first wineries to produce Merlot, Rutherford Hill has begun a new era with Jerry Luper as its winemaker. The 1983 vintage typifies the winery's style of softness and charm.*

Dehlinger Winery: *Every red wine turns out to be exceptional in the hands of the Dehlinger family. The Merlots may be the best overall.*

Inglenook Vineyards: *Once again, after several so-so vintages, Inglenook is moving back into the competition. Classic is the best definition of Inglenook's Merlot.*

Robert Keenan Winery: *Owner Dr. Robert Keenan didn't plan to make Merlot at all, but his winery's first small-scale vintage was so widely praised that Merlot now represents 20 percent of total production. The style is rich in ripe fruit and loaded with tannins, a real ager.*

Clos du Bois: *Probably the biggest Merlot producer in the state, Clos du Bois is also one of the best. The Merlots made under owner Frank Wood's direction are soft, smooth and ready to drink when young.*

Stonegate Winery: *David Spaulding produces no more than several hundred cases of Merlot. The 1980 is*

a collector's item, and the '85 may be a repeat. The '84 comes close, but needs long cellaring.

Gundlach Bundschu Winery: *With the 1982 vintage, winemaker Lance Cutler figured out a way to pack plenty of flavor into his Merlot and still pretend it was luck. The winery's success is the result of excellent grapes and winemaking.*

Stag's Leap Wine Cellars: *Since his first attempt in 1974, winemaster Warren Winiarski has coaxed gentle yet generous fruitiness from his Merlot grapes. The winery presents Merlot in an especially smooth style.*

Pine Ridge Winery: *Located in the Stag's Leap area, Pine Ridge makes a supple kind of Merlot that ages surprisingly well. Partner Gary Andrus skillfully blends in a touch of Cabernet Franc and Cabernet Sauvignon.*

Clos du Val: *Bernard Portet directs the making of what seems like the smoothest, softest, and to many critics, finest Merlot around.*

Jaeger Vineyards: *From grapes grown adjacent to their home south of St. Helena, Bill and Lila Jaeger bottle small quantities of Merlot for their label. They also own Rutherford Hill.*

Simply
Outstanding

Wines from the Heart of the Napa Valley

Raymond Vineyard & Cellar/849 Zinfandel Lane/St. Helena/CA/(707)963-3141

Jordan
Alexander Valley

Producers of estate bottled premium quality California Cabernet Sauvignon and Chardonnay wines.

*O*utstanding Cabernet Sauvignons have come from California vineyards for many decades. In the 1940s and 1950s, the leaders were Beaulieu, Inglenook, Charles Krug and Louis Martini. Today, over 300 wineries offer this red varietal in a range of styles and prices. Sonoma County and Napa Valley are home to the majority of the top-ranked California Cabernets. Some wineries make full-bodied versions with youthful tannins, which age slowly. More are aiming for refined fruity flavors, herbaceous character and early maturity.

CABERNET SAUVIGNON

NORMAN ROBY ✸ RECOMMENDS

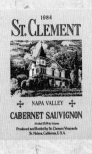

Caymus Vineyards: *Located in Rutherford, the heart of Napa's Cabernet country, Caymus once sold its grapes to other wineries. Since 1972, the winery has earned high marks for its own Cabernets, especially noted for their aging qualities.*

Heitz Cellars: *This winery's Martha's Vineyard Cabernet is coveted for its unique minty, eucalyptus character and ability to age into a complex, smooth, lovely wine. To many collectors, it is without peer.*

Jordan Vineyards: *Denver oilman and geologist Tom Jordan fell in love with wine and built a showcase winery in the Alexander Valley. Since 1976, his winemaker selects the best of the crop and sells the rest. High standards yield high quality.*

Stag's Leap Wine Cellars: *In 1976, at a highly publicized tasting, Stag's Leap Wine Cellars surpassed the leading wineries of Bordeaux. Stag's Leap made fine Cabernets in a rich but supple style from its first vintages.*

Beaulieu Vineyard: *Its Private Reserve remains hallmark wine. Made from the winery's two best vineyards in Rutherford, BV's Reserve is released five years after each vintage, and will last well over a decade.*

Dunn Vineyards: *Randy Dunn, ex-winemaker for Caymus, struck gold under his own name. His Cabernets are among the most coveted. The "Howell Mountain" bottling is more intensely flavored than the "Napa Valley."*

Clos du Val: *A decisive French influence manifests itself in the supple and subtle Cabernets from Clos du Val. The mastermind, Bernard Portet, learned the trade from his father, who was the cellarmaster at Château Lafite in France.*

Mayacamas Vineyards: *From its terraced vineyards high along the eastern mountain range of Napa, Mayacamas has made slow-maturing Cabernets since 1958, rewarding the most patient wine lovers. The wines command high bids at auctions.*

Robert Mondavi Winery: *The Reserve Cabernets rank highly on collectors' lists. Held for three years in new French oak barrels, they age well in the bottle for a decade or more.*

Sterling Vineyards: *The Reserve bottlings have been exceptional in the alternate years of 1975, '77 and '79. Typically, they begin on a low note only to come along seven or eight years later and steal the show.*

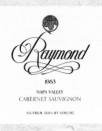

CABERNET SAUVIGNON

William Hill Winery: *William Hill looked for rocky, austere, well-drained hillside vineyards to stress the grape for the quality of wines he wanted to make. His Veeder Peak Vineyard provided the perfect location for medium alcohol content, high acidity and concentrated grape character.*

Markham Vineyards: *Wines that develop slowly to reveal great intensity are their speciality. They hit their peak after eight to ten years. The 1981 is first rate.*

Far Niente: *The estate-bottled Cabernets come from the heart of the Napa Valley, and recent vintages have been acclaimed for their depth and richness, in a soft and accessible style.*

Silver Oak Cellars: *Justin Meyer bottles only Cabernet Sauvignon and releases it after five years. His wines show fine fruit, just the proper amount of oak and excellent bouquet.*

Freemark Abbey: *The Cabernet Bosche, made from grapes of the John Bosche Vineyard, has brought fame to Chuck Carpet and partners since their first vintage in 1970. The entire harvest of the twenty-one-acre vineyard is bottled separately and aged four years before release.*

Conn Creek: *The Cabernets are oak-aged for two years and bottle-aged for another year, producing wines that earn eager bids at the annual Napa Valley Wine Auction. Merlot and Cabernet Franc are added for additional depth and complexity.*

Chimney Rock Winery: *Owner Hack Wilson carved out a beautiful winery along the Silverado Trail. His wines have all been well received, but the Cabernet Sauvignon is destined to become the winery's flagship*

Carmenet: *Built into a hillside, Carmenet is a majestic winery complete with aging caves. Its Cabernet contains Merlot and Cabernet Franc, and in winemaker Jeff Baker's hands, the result is a beauty.*

Ridge: *One of the state's most distinct Cabernets comes from Ridge's small hilltop vineyard. It has a very unusual earthy aroma that needs time to develop harmony.*

Raymond Vineyards: *Long known for its fine Cabernets from Napa Valley, Raymond added a Private Reserve in 1981. It is a stunning, fragrant, well-made example of Cabernet.*

Silverado Vineyards: *In recent vintages winemaker Jack Stuart is winning praise for his stylish Napa Valley Cabernets. The wine stands out with cassis-like fruit, softness and lingering finish.*

Château Potelle: *Jean-Noel and Marketta Fourmeaux du Sartel were professional wine tasters in France before coming to the Alexander Valley. They use French techniques to blend a complex, classic Cabernet with a berry-like bouquet.*

Livingston Vineyards: *Made exclusively from the "Moffett Vineyard," Livingston's Cabernets combine extraordinary depth of flavor with subtle fragrances.*

CABERNET SAUVIGNON

Beringer Vineyards: *Since 1977 the venerable Beringer name has offered stunning Private Reserve Cabernets, which compare favorably with the finest. All vintages are given long oak aging prior to release, but will age long and well in home cellars.*

Groth Vineyards: *This southern Napa Valley winery intends to remain small in size, but its Cabernets are on a grand scale. Winemaker Nils Venge made a name for himself at Villa Mt. Eden for similarly styled Cabernet back in 1974. He'll achieve greater fame for Groth.*

St. Clement: *The winery is a lovely Victorian home just north of St. Helena. Beneath it lies a full-scale facility where winemaker Dennis Johns makes beautifully balanced wines led by his Cabernet vintages.*

Buehler Vineyards: *The Cabernets have always been good, but since Heidi Peterson became winemaker, they are first class. Her father made wines at Beaulieu, and her husband is Montelena's winemaker. If her Cabernets are any indication, she may soon be the star of the family.*

Inglenook Napa Valley: *Since 1984, Inglenook has re-emerged as a superstar of the 1980s. The Diamond Label Reserve is one of the best Cabernets around.*

Burgess Cellars: *Tom Burgess produces wine from grapes grown in the mountains above the Napa Valley. His Cabernets have maximum varietal character, firm oak, good body and a long, complex finish.*

Charles Krug Winery: *This winery's fine record with Cabernet Sauvignon goes back to 1944. Recent vintages have been aromatic and velvety smooth, the result of long aging.*

Fox Mountain: *Sonoma County's Fox Mountain blends Cabernet, Merlot and Cabernet Franc and ages it for at least three years. Aged another five to ten years, it develops very well indeed.*

Diamond Creek Vineyards: *A Cabernet-only winery making three versions from vineyards located high along a mountain ridge in Napa Valley. Each wine is named after the distinctive soil in which its grapes are grown: Red Rock Terrace, Volcanic Hill and Gravelly Meadow.*

Johnson-Turnbull Vineyards: *With only 2,500 cases available each year, this winner is hard to find. It's worth the search. The Cabernet Sauvignon is well structured and emphasizes the distinctive mint-eucalyptus character of the vineyard.*

Durney Vineyards: *After years of producing intensely flavored wines from his mountainside vineyards of Upper Carmel Valley, Bill Durney is rounding out his Cabernet Sauvignons with French oak aging and receiving even greater acclaim.*

Spring Mountain: *The mansion on this winery estate is familiar to all viewers of the television series "Falcon Crest." Since 1972, Spring Mountains Cabernets have shown intense varietal aroma and flavor.*

Monterey. The perfect environment for wine to grow up in. Where the Pacific Ocean and the mountains have been locked in an embrace since the beginning of time. Where a setting sun attracts a lingering gaze. And where life is as relaxed as a day off. It's a place where people have often expressed the sentiment, "I wish there were a way to bottle it."

Monterey. We found a way to bottle it.

*Z*infandel has always enjoyed a favorite-son status and been a sentimental favorite among Californians, perhaps because of the strong Italian influence in our state's history. While its origins are definitely European, the grape is now grown mainly in California and is the most widely cultivated red wine grape. Winemakers value it for its versatility and adaptability, as witnessed by the current White Zinfandel trend. A medium-bodied, deeply colored red wine, Zinfandel tends toward the hearty style, but with an enticing blackberry flavor and a spicy personality.

ZINFANDEL

NORMAN ROBY ✸ RECOMMENDS

Ridge Vineyards: *This winery helped revive and re-establish Zinfandel in the 1960s. Ridge continues its practice of selecting the oldest and best grapes and converting them into several of the finest Zinfandels offered.*

Fetzer Vineyards: *From Mendocino County, Fetzer's Zinfandels are rich in spice and berry-like fruitiness. Look for the Special Reserve for a truly outstanding Zinfandel.*

Clos du Val: *Since 1973, winemaker Bernard Portet has applied his French winemaking skills and developed many successes. His current style tends toward refinement.*

A. Rafanelli & Son: *This small family winery in the Dry Creek Valley has consistently made quintessential Zinfandel. The ripe fruit style, with full berry and black pepper flavors, is perfect when young.*

Kendall Jackson Winery: *Winemaker Jed Steele knows every vine in Mendocino and Lake Counties. Since 1982, he has produced highly polished, lovely renditions of Zinfandel in an emminently appealing style.*

Caymus Vineyards: *Longtime Napa Valley grape growers, Charles and Lorna Wagner and son Chuck make Zinfandel the old-fashioned way: spicy, solid and redolent of berry-like fruit.*

Haywood Winery: *Haywood and winemaker Charles Tolbert produce an intense grape from the steep-sloped, fractured-shale Chamizal Vineyard. Its low yield produces a peppery, intense, berry-flavored Zinfandel.*

Kenwood Vineyards: *Its vintages in the 1980s have made Kenwood one of the state's most respected names. Ripe berries enhanced by spicy oak add up to sophisticated flavors.*

Lytton Springs Winery: *Italian immigrants planted the Hillside Valley Vista Vineyard with Zinfandel eighty-five years ago. It still yields the incredibly rich grapes that are the source of the full-bodied, zesty Lytton Springs Sonoma County Zinfandel.*

Quivera Vineyards: *Its first vintages from the Dry Creek Valley appellation were outstanding. The Quivera Zinfandels offer intense berry flavors and depth, which comes across as textbook-perfect.*

Ravenswood: *Sonoma County winemaker Joel Petterson is a champion of Zinfandel, and recent vintages justify his esteem. He coaxes incredible depth of flavor from his single vineyard bottlings. The "Vintner's Blend" is a delightful "now" wine.*

RIDGE
CALIFORNIA
ZINFANDEL
GEYSERVILLE
1986

64% ZINFANDEL, 10% PETITE SIRAH, 6% CARIGNANE
SONOMA COUNTY   ALCOHOL 13.2% BY VOLUME
PRODUCED AND BOTTLED BY RIDGE VINEYARDS BW-4488
17100 MONTE BELLO RD. BOX A1, CUPERTINO, CALIFORNIA

1986
A. RAFANELLI
ZINFANDEL
DRY CREEK VALLEY
SONOMA COUNTY
UNFILTERED
GROWN, PRODUCED AND BOTTLED BY
A. RAFANELLI WINERY
HEALDSBURG, CALIFORNIA
Alcohol 13.5% by volume • Contains Sulfites

1986 Zinfandel
SONOMA COUNTY
Lytton Springs

KENWOOD
Sonoma Valley
ZINFANDEL
1985
PRODUCED & BOTTLED BY KENWOOD VINEYARDS
KENWOOD, CALIFORNIA
ALCOHOL 12.8% BY VOLUME

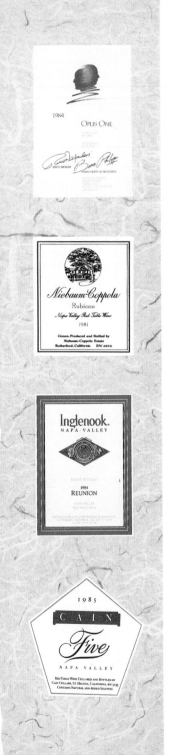

𝒥f winemakers want to use two or more grape varieties without being handcuffed by the minimum varietal percentage regulations, proprietary wines are the way to go. This is especially true when the wine is a red blended along the lines of the finest Bordeaux, made from a combination of Cabernet Sauvignon, Merlot, Cabernet Franc, Malbec and Petit Verdot grapes. In 1974, Phelps began this approach with a wine named Insignia. With the recent entries of wines like Opus One, Rubicon and many others, premium proprietary red wines are a genuine trend.

PREMIUM PROPRIETARY WINES

NORMAN ROBY ✹ RECOMMENDS

Opus One: This wine combines the talents of its owners, the Robert Mondavi family and the Baron Philippe de Rothschild family. Though each vintage has varied more than the norm, the demand has not. The grapes, primarily Cabernet Sauvignon, are grown in the mid-Napa Valley.

Insignia: A special bottling from Joseph Phelps, Insignia aims to be the finest possible wine made by the winery each year. The style leans toward finesse, not heavy-handedness.

Marlstone: A blend of Cabernet Sauvignon, Merlot and Cabernet Franc from Clos du Bois, Marlstone was first made in 1978. The wine has been subtle and supple, a tour de force from winemaker John Hawley.

Trilogy: A great name for a wine made with equal amounts of Cabernet Sauvignon, Merlot and Cabernet Franc, Trilogy is the brainchild of Flora Springs and the Garvey family. They have offered high quality wines from the beginning, but their Trilogy could well catapult them into international prominence.

Cain Five: Joyce and Gerry Cain founded Cain Cellars in 1981 and have been building toward the release of their red proprietary wine, Cain

Five. It is made from all five of the Bordeaux varieties, and the first vintage, 1985, is right on target.

Rubicon: The grapes for this blended red come from the historic Niebaum vineyard once belonging to Inglenook, now owned by Francis Ford Coppola. The long-awaited first vintage of 1980 was somewhat disappointing, but newer versions have rewarded those able to locate a few bottles.

Lyeth: Lyeth's red and white wines are proprietary blends; the owner follows the Bordeaux winemaking philosophy to the letter. The Lyeth red comes from the Estate vineyards in northern Sonoma County. Lyeth's first vintage from 1981 was fine, but the quality has improved each year.

Reunion: A red wine from Inglenook, Reunion is rather unusual in that it is 100 percent Cabernet Sauvignon. It is, however, a blend in that it is made from grapes grown in three different Rutherford vineyards.

Reserve Alexandre: Another fine, harmonious blend of Cabernet Sauvignon, Cabernet Franc and Merlot, this one, made by Geyser Peak, is new on the market. It reflects rapid changes being made by that winery.

Inglenook.
N A P A · V A L L E Y

We invite you to visit our historic stone winery in Rutherford and to taste our award-winning wines. Tours and tastings daily from 10-5.

TO SEND A GIFT OF INGLENOOK-NAPA VALLEY
CALL 1-800-272-5883

Inglenook-Napa Valley Rutherford, California - USA

1988. THE START OF SOME VERY GOOD YEARS.

The time has come. Three years have passed since Rémy Martin acquired Charles Heidsieck. Years of work, of change. And now, today, it's time for the new Charles Heidsieck to be released.

wo kinds of dessert wine are available today. The first is a white wine labeled Late Harvest or Select Late Harvest, most often made from Johannisberg Riesling. Botrytis cinerea, a naturally occurring beneficial mold, concentrates the sugar level in this wine and imparts an exotic fragrance and flavor of honey, almonds and ripe apricots. The second kind is known as fortified wine, such as Sherry and Port, and is produced by adding a small amount of brandy to the wine. A small glass of either type with dessert, or even *as* dessert, makes a lovely finale to gracious dining.

DESSERT WINES

NORMAN ROBY ⬟ RECOMMENDS

Château St. Jean: *Winemaker Dick Arrowood's special Rieslings have dazzled connoisseurs for several years. In 1983, the winery made supreme dessert wines from both Riesling and Gewurztraminer. The richest are sold in the 375 ml bottle.*

Quady Winery: *Andy Quady specializes in Port wines and is a leader in the field. He produces a wine called Essencia from an old vineyard of Orange Muscat, which is lightly fortified to retain the enticing aroma of orange blossoms. The 1984 Black Muscat Elysium, with a floral nose and a fig-like taste, is as delightful.*

Schramsberg Vineyard: *Reminding us that sparkling wine can be right with dessert, Schramsberg offers its Crémant Demi-Sec, with a subtle yet delightful personality.*

Beaulieu Vineyard: *One of the world's oldest wines is a fortified Muscat Frontignan. For years BV has given its version special care and aging in small oak barrels, and oenophiles have finally discovered it.*

Joseph Phelps Vineyards: *Owner Joe Phelps loves to offer unusual wines. When the climate cooperates, his winery makes rich Select Late Harvest Rieslings. The 1982 is legendary, the 1985 a worthy successor.*

Bonny Doon Vineyards: *A small winery in the Santa Cruz Mountains, Bonny Doon makes headlines with every new wine it produces. Among the most unusual is its dessert wine made from grapes frozen for several months. Called "Vin de Glacière," this wine is simply wonderful.*

Shenandoah Vineyards: *Up in Amador County where Zinfandel is king, Leon Sobel displays a real knack with dessert wines. The Orange Muscat is a musk-oil, orange-blossom beauty. The winery also has excellent Black Muscat and Port.*

Pat Paulsen Vineyards: *Comedian Pat Paulsen relaxes in his Sonoma County ranch surrounded by vineyards. Among his many fine wines, the slightly sweet, intensely fragrant Muscat Canelli is superb.*

Château De Baun: *Ken De Baun has the largest planting in the world of a new grape hybrid called Symphony. With Paulsen winemaker Jamie Meves, he has bottled music for your palate with this versatile white grape. The 1984 Finale is outstanding.*

Norman Roby is director of wine education at the California Culinary Academy and a columnist for *The Wine Spectator.*

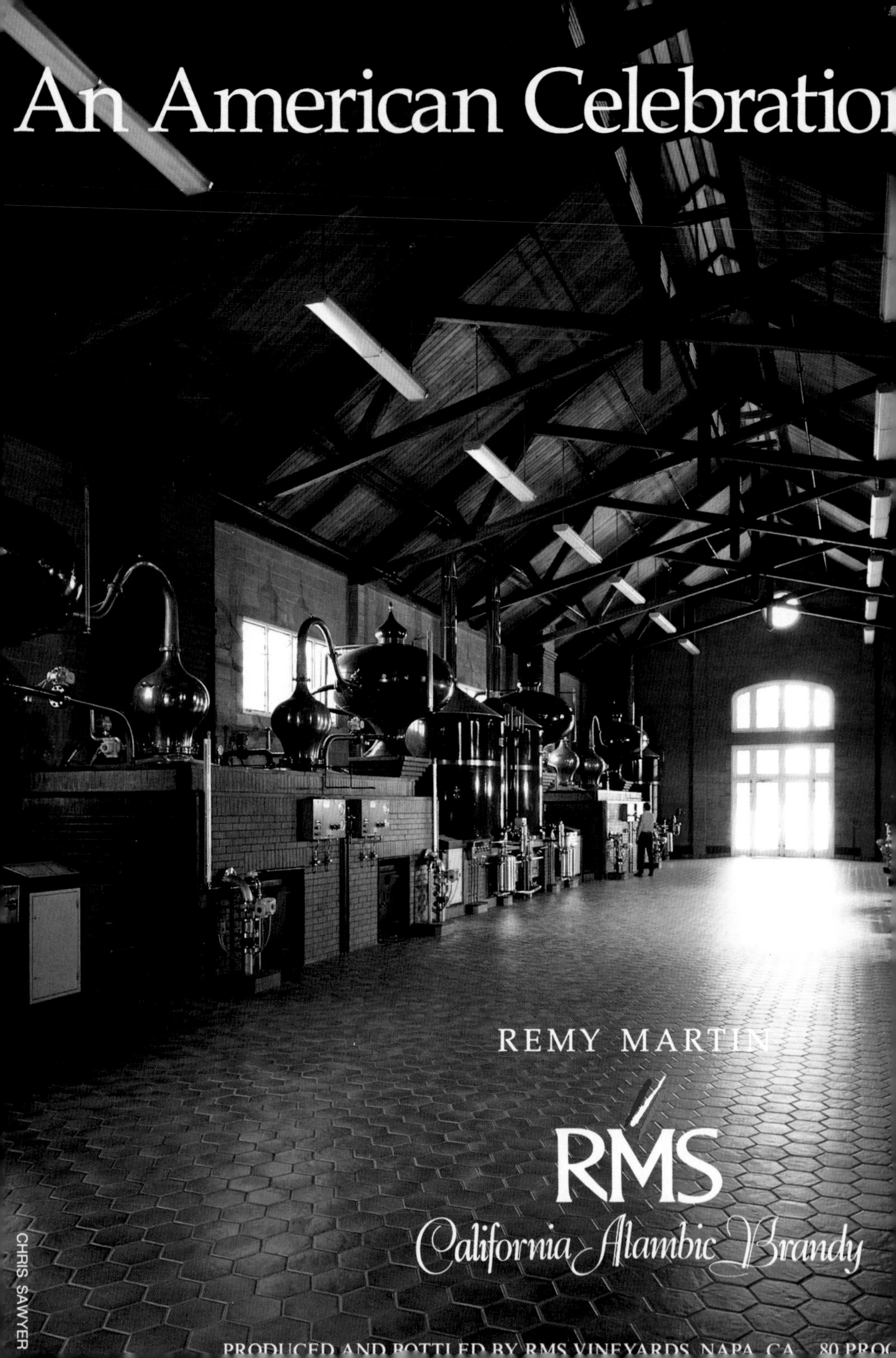

An American Celebration

REMY MARTIN

RMS
California Alambic Brandy

CHRIS SAWYER

SPIRITS & LIQUEURS

BY GERALD D. BOYD

Drink Less, But Drink The Very Best

TODAY'S EMPHASIS ON MODERATE DRINKING IS A CHALLENGE TO BE more creative and versatile in what we consume. Spirits and liqueurs come in so many varieties, styles and flavors that they more than meet this challenge. As you discover the many ways to use them in food and drink recipes, you will begin to appreciate higher-quality products. There are degrees of excellence, whether you're buying aged rums, single malt scotches, flavored vodkas or imported liqueurs, and subtle differences among the best brands. What you prefer is a matter of taste, but quality should be the first criterion.

WHISKEY

WHISKEY, SPELLED "WHISKY" BY SCOTS AND Canadians, is by definition a "brown spirit," distilled from a select recipe (often called a mash bill) of grains. Whiskeys differ in many subtle ways, but the two major distinctions are determined by the type of still used and the grains in the recipe.

Single malt scotch is an example of whiskey made from one grain, in this case barley, produced in small batches in a pot still. Irish whiskey is also made in a pot still, but the grain recipe may include small quantities of oats, rye and wheat.

Among the best-known Irish whiskeys are Old Bushmills, John Jameson, Paddy, Power's and Murphy's, which is blended for the American market. Black Bush, distilled by Old Bushmills, is similar to a malt whiskey but it contains grain spirits in the blend.

Scottish immigrants built the Canadian whiskey business, although the Canadian whiskey of today bears

little resemblance to Scotch whiskey. Often referred to as "rye," Canadian whiskey is made from cereal grains, primarily corn, with about 10 percent rye and a little barley added to the blend. All Canadian whiskeys are blends and are made in continuous stills. Among the most popular are Canadian Club, Crown Royal, Seagram's V.O., Lord Calvert, Black Velvet, Schenley OFC and Windsor Supreme.

Although most American whiskeys are blends, there are also a number of straight whiskeys. The major difference is in the percentages of various grains used (predominantly corn), and how they are aged. By Federal law, a blended whiskey must contain at least 20 percent 100-proof straight whiskey by volume. Seagram's 7 Crown dominates the field. Also popular are Calvert, Carstairs, Park & Tilford, Schenley Reserve, Antique, Kessler and Four Roses. American blends enjoy a very strong regional brand loyalty.

Straight whiskey cannot be blended with other whiskeys before aging or bottling. Furthermore, the mash bill blend must consist of at least 51 percent of a single grain.

Bourbon is the best-known straight whiskey produced in the United States, usually from 70 percent corn. It is made in a handful of states, but the best bourbons are considered those from Kentucky.

Bourbons must be aged in new charred-oak casks for at least two years, although many are aged longer. "Sour mash" refers to the use of a sour-mash yeasting process, and may or may not appear as a label term. Maker's Mark and Old Fitzgerald add wheat to their mash bill, resulting in a smoother bourbon with greater finesse. Other quality bourbons include Jim Beam, Wild Turkey, Old Grand-Dad, Ancient Age, I.W. Harper, Benchmark, Old Forester and Weller's Special Reserve.

Tennessee whiskey is similar to bourbon, except that it is filtered through sugar-maple charcoal and aged for a minimum of four years to give it a smooth taste. Jack Daniel's is the leader, but George A. Dickel is also a fine Tennessee whiskey.

SCOTCH

TWO TYPES OF SCOTCH WHISKEY ARE PRODUCED: single malt and blended. Single malt scotch is distilled from pure water and malted barley permeated with varying amounts of peat. Malt whiskey, as it is often called, is the true whiskey of Scotland.

Blended scotch, a relatively recent innovation, is a proprietary house blend of a number of different malt whiskeys and a few grain whiskeys. Top blended scotches include Johnnie Walker, Chivas Regal, Dewar's, Cutty Sark, Cluny, Black & White, Pinch, Desmond & Duff, The Famous Grouse, Haig & Haig, J&B Rare, Bell's, Teacher's, Usher's and White Horse.

Of the two scotch whiskeys, malt whiskey is the more interesting because of its stylistic diversity. Its unique character depends on the source of the barley, the malting process, the amount of peat used to fire the ovens that dry the barley, the water source, and the size and shape of the still. Scotland's malt distilleries are located in four major areas: Highland, Lowland, Island and Cambeltown.

HIGHLAND MALTS: *Highland malts, made near the River Spey, are usually well balanced in flavor and body, with a pleasing touch of pungent peat. Quality Highland malts include Cardhu, Glenmorangie, The Macallan, Knockando, Mortlach, Glen Grant Glenlivet and Glenury Royal. The Glenlivet and Glenfiddich, top sellers in the United States, are Highland malts.*

LOWLAND MALTS: *The few Lowland malts made are among the lightest, both in color and flavor, with just a touch of peat. At present, Auchentoshan and Rosebank are the most commonly available.*

ISLAND MALTS: *Islay, off the Atlantic coast, produces the heaviest and most distinctive Island malts. For some malt drinkers, Laphroaig, with its pronounced peat flavor, is the quintessential Islay malt. Less intense, with a little more finesse, are Bunnahabhain, Bruichladdich and Lagavulin.*

CAMBELTOWN MALTS: *Southeast of Islay is Cambeltown, the smallest of the four producing areas. Only Springbank continues to distill malt whiskey.*

MYTHOLOGY

If you've been drinking a fine blended scotch like Chivas, Black Label, or Pinch, the idea that there's something even smoother, something even more distinctive, sounds like pure fantasy.

REALITY

But there is something smoother. Something more distinctive. Glenfiddich. The pure malt scotch that isn't blended with grain whiskies. Just try it once. And you'll find mythology is reality.

To send a gift of Glenfiddich anywhere in the U.S., call 1-800-238-4373. Void where prohibited by law.

VODKA

GIN

ONE OF THE YOUNGEST SPIRITS, GIN DATES TO THE mid-seventeenth century. Now a favorite the world over, gin was created by Dr. Sylvius, a Dutch professor of medicine, as an inexpensive diuretic and purifying tonic for his fellow Dutchmen. He called his tonic *genièvre*, the French word for juniper. The Dutch shortened it to *genever*, which they use today for what we call gin.

To make gin, distillers, following a closely guarded formula, produce a pure neutral spirit from juniper, derived from the berries of evergreen trees. The spirit is then re-distilled in a pot still to add more flavor. Some distillers prefer to hang the flavoring agents, called botanicals, above the alcohol and let the vapors pick up the flavor subtleties as they rise through. Some popular flavoring botanicals are cinnamon, coriander, angelica root, licorice, bitter almonds, and dried orange and lemon.

Gin does not require aging: in fact, you can drink gin the day it was made. Wood-aging for a short period is sometimes used to give gin a light yellow color. These gins are known as golden gins.

LONDON DRY: *The most popular of gins, real London Dry is either made in England or elsewhere under British license. London Dry is known for its dry and tangy fresh juniper flavor. The most popular English-made London Dry gins are Tanqueray and Beefeater. Also in demand is the smooth, mellow Bombay Dry, bottled in London since 1761.*

Other London Dry gins, made in the United States, include Gordon's, Gilbey's, Calvert, Booth's and Bellows. Seagram's produces a London Extra Dry as well as Burnett's White Satin.

IN RUSSIA, WHERE *ZHIZNENNIA VODKA HAS BEEN A* popular spirit since the fourteenth century, no one would ever think of mixing vodka with anything. The classic Russian way to drink it is ice-cold and straight up—preferably from a bottle that has been frozen in a block of ice. But since the 1940s vodka has been popular in the U.S. as a cocktail and highball spirit.

Vodka can be made from any material containing starch. Today, mostly corn is used, though potatoes are still used in Poland and Russia. A mash is pressure-cooked, then mixed with water and fermented. Distillation follows in a continuous still at a high proof of 190 to extract maximum flavoring elements. The new spirit is purified by charcoal filtration and bottled.

AMERICAN VODKA: *U.S. vodka production began when the Smirnoff family, which had established a fortune and reputation for charcoal-filtered vodka in their native Russia, fled during the Revolution and set up business in Connecticut. Today, Smirnoff is owned by Heublein.*

SCANDINAVIAN VODKA: *Traditionally, Eastern Europe is known for the best vodka. In recent years, though, Scandinavian vodkas have come into their own. More neutral than Eastern European vodkas, Finland's Finlandia, Norway's Vikin Fjord and Sweden's classic, subtle Absolut appeal to the American taste for mild-tasting vodka.*

EASTERN EUROPEAN VODKA: *Polish vodkas have a full, pungent, yet distinctive taste. The most popular brand is Wyborowa, 80 and 100 proof. Others include Monopolowa by Baczewski, and Luksusowa, a potato vodka.*

FLAVORED VODKA: *Long a popular drink in Poland and Russia, flavored vodka recently has become a hot item in the West. Traditional Polish flavored vodka, such as that from Kord Zubrowka, is infused with bison grass, which the Poles claim will give the drinker the strength of a bison. Sweden's Absolut makes Peppar, flavored with red and green peppers. Other popular flavorings include black pepper, cherry, juniper, lemon and green walnut.*

ABSOLUT
ountry of Sweden
PEPPAR

Absolut Peppar is made
...tial peppers ...
a... ...m gr...
...f...
The ...tilling and f...
is an a... ...swea...
...ating ba... ...n 4...
...dka has be... ...der the nam...
Absolut ... ...879.

80 PROOF
PEPPER FLAVORED VODKA,
PRODUCED AND BOTTLED IN SWEDEN. 1.0 LITER.
IMPORTED
IMPORTER AND SOLE DISTRIBUTOR FOR THE U.S.
CARILLON IMPORTERS LTD., TEANECK, N.J.

ABSOLUT MARY.

TEQUILA

THE ORIGINS OF TEQUILA CAN BE TRACED BACK TO the Aztecs who produced *pulque*, a milky alcoholic beverage made from the agave plant so abundant in rural Mexico. The Spanish brought the skill of distillation with them when they conquered Mexico. They distilled *pulque* into mezcal, a clear, brandy-like spirit with a strong, earthy, herbal flavor. Eventually, mezcal (or *pulque*; no one is sure which) was refined through distillation into a spirit known today as tequila.

Tequila is made from the blue agave, which may stand ten feet tall, and has a pineapple-shaped heart that can weigh up to 150 pounds. The agave hearts are chopped and steamed into a sweet concentrate, which is fermented about two days.

A double distillation in pot stills follows, producing a raw spirit of about 104 proof. This "white" or "silver" spirit is reduced with water to 80 proof and bottled.

GOLD TEQUILA: *"Gold" tequila has been aged in oak casks for nine months or more. Since there is no government control on the aging, the coloring of gold tequila may be hastened a little with the addition of caramel.*

ANEJO: *The best tequila is known as anejo, which means "aged." Anejo may rest in oak for three to ten years, until the right character and flavor are achieved. Connoisseurs think nothing of paying the same price for anejo as that asked for a premium cognac.*

White (silver) and gold tequilas are available from such quality producers as Herradura, Two Fingers, Don Emilio, Montezuma, Monte Alban and, of course, Jose Cuervo and Sauza. A few of these also market a mezcal. Anejo tequilas are more rare, with one of the best available from Herradura.

RUM

BORN AS A TONIC TO HELP ENGLISH SETTLERS COPE with the rigors of life in the West Indies, rum, not raw sugar, was the first product of island sugar cane. The name is thought to have come from the English country slang expression "rumbullion," the roaring noise inside the head caused by the drink. Rum became the spirit of the islands by the mid-eighteenth century.

It was perhaps inevitable that rum became the favored drink of the pirates who roamed the Caribbean. The notorious pirate chantey "Fifteen Men on a Dead Man's Chest" had as its refrain, "Yo ho ho and a bottle of rum." The English navy once carried rum among its rations, as it was thought to prevent scurvy; today's rum punch called "grog" gets its name from the daily dose of rum and water administered by the English Admiral nicknamed "Old Grog."

Rum is the distillate of fermented molasses, sugar cane syrup and sugar cane juice. A mash is fermented and sent through a continuous or column still. The clear raw spirit is matured and mellowed in small oak casks for six months to twelve years, then bottled at 80 to 90 proof. Although they are made elsewhere, the best rums are from the Caribbean.

Rums are made in two main styles—light and dark. Light rums are perfect for warm-weather fruit-based drinks such as daiquiris and Mai Tais, while dark rums are favored for drinks traditionally served in winter, like eggnog and hot buttered rum. The classic, potent planter's punch, however, could be made with nothing but cool, dark rum. Both styles are refreshing served straight over ice with lime.

LIGHT RUM: *Often labeled "Silver" or "White," light rums are light in body and subtle in flavor. Produced in the islands originally settled by the Spanish, such as Puerto Rico and Cuba, light rums are favored in the United States because they are well suited for mixed drinks.*

Puerto Rico's Bacardi is the top-selling brand in the U.S. Other popular Puerto Rican rums include Ronrico, Ron Castillo, Palo Viejo and Captain Morgan Spiced Rum. Another type of light rum is Demerara, from Guyana. Lemon Hart,

ABSOLUT TWIST.

Guyana's legendary 151-proof rum, is used in high-octane cocktails like the Zombie.

MEDIUM RUMS: *Medium-colored rums stay in the cask for up to three years and get their deep amber hue from the addition of caramel. Usually labeled "Amber" or "Gold," these fuller rums are richer in flavor, sometimes with a little sweetness. Bacardi Gold Reserve from Puerto Rico and Mount Gay and Cockspur are quality medium rums, as are Cruzan, Montego Bay and Old St. Croix from the Virgin Islands.*

DARK RUMS: *Less popular, but no less appealing, are the rich, full-bodied dark rums of Jamaica. Made from molasses, with additions from previous distillations, Jamaican rums are round and flavor-packed. The best known are Myers's Jamaican Punch, Appleton and Lemon Hart Jamaica.*

FRENCH ISLAND RUM: *The so-called French Island rums of Haiti and Martinique have a more refined bouquet and flavor because they are distilled from fresh cane juice, not molasses, and are aged, like fine cognac, in oak casks. Negrita and Clement are Martinique's best-known rums. Haiti's Barbancourt is available in Three Star, Five Star, and fifteen-year-old.*

SPECIALTY DRINKS

SOME DRINKS CANNOT BE PLACED INTO ANY SPECIfic category. Vermouth, for example, is not a wine, although it has a wine base. And it is not a liqueur, even though it is flavored. For the sake of simplicity, these in-between spirits belong to the "specialty drinks" group.

With its bittersweet herbal flavor, vermouth is a basic aperitif. The white, usually drier than the red, is used alone with a twist or as a mixer for cocktails such as the Martini. Heavier and sweeter, the red is mostly used as an ingredient in such drinks as the Manhattan, although it can stand alone.

Noilly Prat is a notable French vermouth. Among the best known Italian vermouths are Cinzano and Martini & Rossi.

Most aperitifs are variations on vermouth, with a wine base and a flavor that comes from herbs and bitter plants. Some believe that bitters are a digestive, a healthful tonic and even an aphrodisiac. On their own, bitters such as Angostura, Underberg and Fernet Branca are well-known digestives.

Italy's most popular aperitif is Campari. Like all aperitifs, it has a secret recipe. However, we do know that it is made from aromatic herbs and spices steeped in a spirit, then aged in oak vats.

The French, traditional leaders in food and drink, have their own favorite aperitifs. Among the most famous are Pernod, Ricard, Lillet and Dubonnet. Sweet anise-flavored aperitifs, Pernod and Ricard are descendants of Absinthe, the potent 19th century "pastis" that was eventually outlawed. Poured over ice and water, they become cloudy like Absinthe.

A subtle aperitif with a hint of orange, Lillet comes from south of Bordeaux. The base wine is infused with herbs and other botanicals, then adjusted for sweetness.

Dubonnet is another popular French aperitif. Available in Blanc and Rouge, it is sweet and aromatic and, like vermouth, made with an infusion of botanicals in a base wine. In fact, if Dubonnet is not available, a blend of equal parts of white and red vermouth makes a satisfactory substitute.

From England comes Pimm's No. 1 Cup. It has a gin base to which are added liqueurs, herbs and citrus extracts. Produced in London, Pimm's is a popular drink served in a tall glass over ice, sometimes with soda or tonic.

Another aperitif that is catching on is Schnapps, the German name for aquavit. Aquavit is a dry spirit made from grains or potatoes and flavored with caraway seed.

On its own, plain Schnapps is not that popular in the United States. The American taste runs more to Schnapps with such enticing flavors as Peach Basket, Strawberry Patch, Pina Colada, Raspberry Ridge or Old Style Rootbeer. Schnapps can also be flavored with peppermint, apricot, pear, apple and blackberry.

Flavored Schnapps are produced by the major cordial companies like Leroux, Dekuyper, Hiram Walker and Bols.

Finally, there is Moet & Chandon's Petite Liqueur, a delightful blend of aged Champagne and cognac. Packaged in a miniature Champagne bottle, complete with cork, it is a sweet, slightly sparkling liqueur with a complex, mellow flavor of caramel. Petite Liqueur is best enjoyed chilled and served straight up, as an aperitif or an after-dinner drink.

ABSOLUT
Country of Sweden
VODKA®

This superb *
was distilled from grain g*
in the rich fields of southern S*
It has been produced at the fam*
old distilleries near *hus
in accordance with more than
400 years of Swedish tradition.
Vodka has been sold under the name
Absolut Since 1879.

80 PROOF
PRODUCED AND BOTTLED IN SWEDEN 1.0 LITER (33.8 FL. OZ.)

IMPORTED

IMPORTER AND SOLE DISTRIBUTOR FOR THE U.S.
CARILLON IMPORTERS LTD., NEW YORK, N.Y.

ABSOLUT BRAVO.

FOR GIFT DELIVERY ANYWHERE CALL 1-800-CHEER-UP (EXCEPT WHERE PROHIBITED BY LAW)
80 AND 100 PROOF/100% GRAIN NEUTRAL SPIRITS (ABSOLUT COUNTRY OF SWEDEN) © 1985 CARILLON IMPORTERS LTD., TEANECK, NJ.

BRANDY

MOST SPIRITS CALLED BRANDY ARE DISTILLED FROM grape wine, but there are also brandies made from various kinds of fruit like cherries, apples and plums. *Eaux-de-vie*, distilled fruit spirits, are often classified as brandies, but for the purist, only a brandy distilled from grapes merits the name.

COGNAC

"ALL COGNAC IS BRANDY, BUT NOT ALL BRANDY IS cognac," is an axiom with a specific point—there are a lot of brandies, but only those grown in the Cognac region of France may be called cognac. The Cognac region is in west central France near the Atlantic Ocean, just north of Bordeaux. Of its six subregions, the best are Grande Champagne and Petite Champagne. Cognac is a blend of brandies, often coming from several of the subregions; a Fine Champagne is a blend of Grand Champagne and Petite Champagne brandies.

Cognac is distilled twice in a pot still and aged, first in new oak casks, then in older ones. Very old cognac is often moved into large glass demijohns to prevent bitterness resulting from prolonged wood aging.

A cognac must be aged in wood for at least two years before it is exported to the United States. A three-star cognac is one aged a minimum of three years. The three-year minimum also applies to V.S. (Very Superior). V.S.O.P. (Very Superior Old Pale) and V.O. (Very Old) must be aged at least four years. Napoleon Grande Reserve, Paradis and Extra Vieille require a six-year minimum, though most are aged in wood much longer. Once bottled, cognacs do not age further. Courvoisier, Hennessy and Martell are the major distillers of cognac, but there are others offering a range of premium cognacs. These include Hine, Delamain, Otard, Camus, Remy Martin and Salignac. Since many distillers prefer their own premium terms, Napoleon cognacs, such as Courvoisier Napoleon, are often not labeled that way. Martell's Cordon Bleu, Hennessy's Bras d'Or and Polignac's Reserve Prince Hubert are popular examples.

Luxury cognacs, often special lots from the distillery's private collection or *paradis*, are well-aged mellow spirits with great depth of flavor, often lavishly packaged in beautiful cut-crystal decanters. Among the best luxury cognacs are Remy Martin Louis XIII Grand Fine and Remy Martin X.O., Hennessy X.O. Baccarat and Hennessy Paradis, Martell Reserve du Fondateur, Hine Triomphe, Courvoisier V.O.C. Fine Champagne and Delamain Daum Crystal.

ARMAGNAC

BECAUSE ARMAGNAC IS A SMALL, LANDLOCKED rural region, its excellent spirit is not as well known as cognac. Located south of Bordeaux, Armagnac produces less brandy than Cognac does. Armagnac is distilled once in a small continuous still, which generates a higher concentration of flavor components than does a pot still distillation and gives armagnac its characteristic flavor.

Armagnac has an aging system similar to that of cognac. The minimum is eighteen months in oak, with V.O. and V.S.O.P. and Reserve requiring a minimum of four years, while Hors d'Age, Napoleon, Extra and Vieille Reserve must be aged at least five years.

With both cognac and armagnac, the law requires only a minimum aging. Thus a V.S.O.P., the most popular type, may in fact contain brandies much older than the required minimum of four years. However, unlike cognac, armagnac does have vintage-dated bottles as well as brandies. Many distillers date the label with the year the spirit was made as well as the year it was bottled. Premium brands include Sempe, Samalens, Janneau, Larresingle, Marquis de Montesquiou, Marquis de Cassuade and De Montal.

What did you do to deserve Beefeater?

BEEFEATER

IMPORTED ENGLISH GIN

The best of times deserve the best of taste.

94 Proof. 100% grain neutral spirits. The Buckingham Wile Company, N.Y. © 1988.

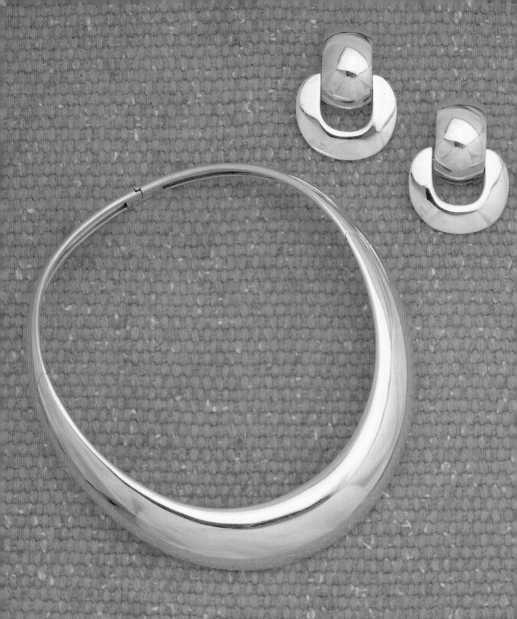

LIQUEURS

IN THE SALONS OF NINETEENTH-CENTURY ENGLAND and Europe, it was common to serve a mild digestive to settle the stomach after a long, multi-course meal. The origin of liqueurs, however, can be traced to the sixteenth century when the liqueur Danzig Gold-wasser first appeared. Made from exotic blends of herbs, barks and seeds, the first liqueurs were valued for their medicinal properties, although their restorative powers were more imaginary than real.

For many years, Americans preferred the term "cordial," derived from the Latin word meaning "belonging to the heart." In Europe and the United Kingdom, the accepted term was liqueur, also from the Latin ("to dissolve"), which more closely fits the definition of the beverage.

In simple terms, a liqueur is a sweetened spirit base (a natural grain alcohol or a grape *eau-de-vie*) flavored with a natural plant agent. The production of liqueurs is complicated and time consuming, often involving many steps and requiring expensive and scarce raw materials. There are two basic methods: maceration and distillation. Maceration is the simplest, soaking the flavoring substances in the spirit base until the alcohol is infused with their flavors. Maceration is used to produce liqueurs made from soft fruits like strawberries and raspberries, although not exclusively.

Distillation is usually reserved for plants and herbs. The aim is not to produce flavored alcohol, but to collect aromatic vapors and condense them into a liquid. The process often requires successive distillations to extract the essential oils of the raw material. Only pot stills are used.

After distillation or maceration, the liqueur is sweetened with a simple sugar syrup or sometimes honey. Water or neutral spirits are also added to adjust the alcohol content to between 25 and 40 percent. Finally, coloring, obtained from either certified food colors or an infusion of plants and fruits, is added to many liqueurs.

Distillers guard the secret formulas for their liqueurs very closely, sometimes for centuries. It is said that the formula for the famous monastery herbal liqueur Chartreuse, first devised in 1605, is known only to three monks at any one time.

There are four basic types of liqueurs: herbal, seed and plant, fruit, a loosely defined group using brandy or whiskey as a base, and the latest addition, cream liqueurs.

HERBAL LIQUEURS

IN THE MIDDLE AGES, CERTAIN PLANTS, HERBS AND spices were used by alchemists for medicinal properties. From these crude medicines, liqueurs were created. Many of the classic herbal liqueurs, such as Benedictine and Chartreuse, were made in monasteries as curatives.

Benedictine, originally made by Benedictine monks, is thought to date from 1510, which makes it one of the oldest liqueurs. Benedictine production was placed in secular hands in 1863, where it remains today. A proprietary blend of twenty-seven ingredients, it is dark amber in color, medium sweet, with a soft flavor like vanilla, almond and honey. In 1938, Benedictine created B&B, a blend of the liqueur and aged cognac, which is drier and more like brandy.

Chartreuse is made in two styles: the original green, lightly sweet with a complex spicy-peppery flavor, and the sweeter, lower alcohol yellow. Both green and yellow are also available in a limited V.E.P. (aged for twelve years) bottling.

Other popular herbal liqueurs include the Basque Izarra, German Jaegermeister and the Italian Liquore Galliano, made from anise as well as other fragrant herbs. The assertive herbal Strega from southern Italy is much like the French herbal liqueurs.

Plant & Seed Liqueurs

ALSO KNOWN FOR THEIR RESTORATIVE PROPERTIES, seed and plant liqueurs differ in that they are often flavored by just one substance, such as aniseed, mint, caraway or coffee.

The list of plant and seed liqueurs is lengthy. Among the best known are Anisette, made from aniseed, not licorice; Crème de Menthe, made from mint leaves in both clear and green styles; Crème de Cacao, made from vanilla pods and cocoa beans; Vandermint, made from mint and chocolate; Kahlua, a Mexican liqueur made from coffee, with a chocolate-like flavor; and Amaretto di Saronno, made not from almonds but from crushed apricot pits.

Others include Sambuca Romano, made from the elder flower, which is similar in character to aniseed; Kummel, made from caraway or cumin seeds; Truffles chocolate liqueur and Marie Brizard's Chocolat; Cheri-Suisse, a chocolate-cherry liqueur; Tia Maria, a Jamaican coffee liqueur; Peachtree Schnapps, a natural peach flavor; Frangelico, made from hazelnuts; and Crème de Noyaux, similar to Amaretto since it is made from apricot or peach pits.

Fruit Liqueurs

SINCE CAPTURING A TRUE FRUIT FLAVOR IS OFTEN an elusive exercise, fruit liqueurs are perhaps the most difficult to make.

The most common fruit liqueurs are made from oranges. Grand Marnier, based on cognac and orange essence, is one of the best known. The most popular Grand Marnier, Cordon Rouge, a/blend of three-to-five-year-old cognac and orange essence, matures in large oak uprights for nine to twelve months before bottling.

Another well-known French liqueur is Cointreau, produced from the peels of bitter and sweet oranges. Mandarine Napoleon, from Belgium, is similar to Grand Marnier but has a distinctive tangerine and herb flavor. Curacao, Triple Sec and Spain's Liquor Gran Torres are other notable orange liqueurs.

Second in number only to citrus-flavored liqueurs are those made from cherries. The best-known are Peter Heering from Denmark and Cherry Marnier from France.

The flavor cornucopia of fruit liqueurs also includes raspberry, blackberry, strawberry, banana, apricot and peach (Pêcher Mignon is made from white peaches). Exotic fruit liqueurs such as La Grande Passion, made of passion fruit, and Midori, made in Japan from melons, have also made a splash. Cassis, a black currant drink, is actually too low in alcohol for legitimate standing as a liqueur.

Brandy & Whiskey Liqueurs

THIS SPECIALTY GROUP DIFFERS IN THAT THE PROducer adds a bit of grape brandy or grain whiskey to flavor an otherwise bland high-proof spirit.

As mentioned earlier, Grand Marnier is the premier brandy-based liqueur. Made mostly of Benedictine, Grand Marnier also contains 40 percent six-year-old cognac in the blend. Other popular brandy liqueurs include Metaxa from Greece and the lesser-known Italian Tuaca, which reputedly gets its body from a small percentage of milk added to the final blend.

Popular Scottish liqueurs include Drambuie, a blend of Scotch whiskey, herbs and honey, and the less intense Lochan Ora. Irish Mist, also based on a recipe of herbs and honey, is lighter and drier. The best-known American whiskey liqueur is Southern Comfort, with a sweet peachy flavor and subtle citrus notes.

Epicurean Rendezvous

*gratefully acknowledges the support
of the following sponsors:*

RESTAURANT INDEX